MY LITTLE PLAGUE JOURNAL

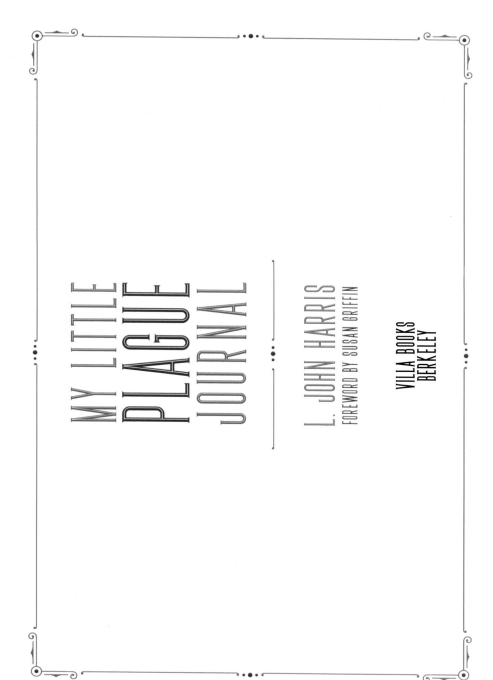

MY LITTLE PLAGUE JOURNAL

L. JOHN HARRIS

FOREWORD BY SUSAN GRIFFIN

VILLA BOOKS
BERKELEY

ISBN: 979-8-88525-688-9

Distributed to the book trade by Itasca Books
Itascabooks.com

Published by Villa Books
1569 Solano Ave., Suite 201
Berkeley, CA 94707

DEDICATED TO THE FUTURE

CONTENTS

Memento mori* and obey the Lord.
Art and religion love the somber chord.

— Robert Frost

*Remember you must die.
Gather ye rosebuds while ye may.
Carpe diem.
Tick tock.

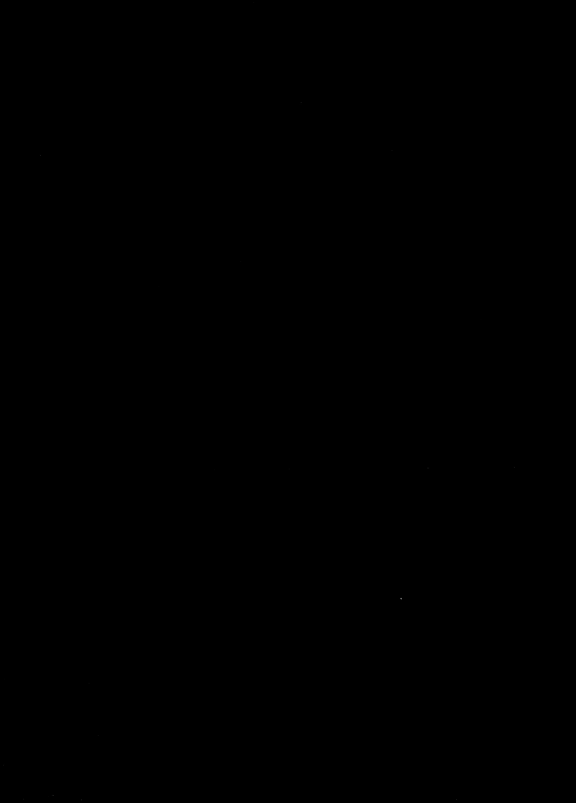

FOREWORD

This quite pleasing though unconventional "journal" captures both in content and form the profoundly disorienting, and yet in so many ways fruitful, experience of the famous coronavirus pandemic that began thirty years ago, in 2020. I recently came across this work by writer and artist L. John Harris while browsing in one of the brick and mortar bookstores that lately have become so fashionable.

If the book is shaped by a wildly eccentric sense of humor, this does not lessen the sense that here you will find a revealing mirror of what so many of us felt during that siege, separated as we were from friends and family, people in public places, cafés, restaurants, concert halls and markets. Isolated in our houses, if not stir crazy, we were certainly disoriented. Yet, as with the author, if one paid close attention, the mood that occupied us (some might say, held us captive) had a creative side. Indeed, as far as I have been able to determine, our collective but isolated inner lives resembled the surrealism of the last century, a movement in literature and art that arose in the sway of two disasters, the First World War, and the lethal influenza pandemic of 1918. A mood in which inner thoughts, phantasms, symbols, dreams, imaginary fears, and odd obsessions (as with the author's almost fetishistic interest in potatoes) occupied as much if not more space in our minds as did the three dimensional issues that together comprise what we call "reality."

Still there is one decidedly realistic element in this document and that is the author's blazing satire depicting the infamous Donald Trump, whom I have continued to study myself with an eye to preventing a ghostly return. But here, again, the work truthfully captures the obsession so many of us had in those days with a man who came perilously close to destroying democracy; and who during his tenure as President did his best to ensure the novel Corona virus would spread unchecked while, at the same time, ignoring the threat of an increasingly dangerous global warming. Mr. Trump belongs in this book if only because he seems, even decades later, like a mythic monster, unreal and yet as disturbing as his voluminous lies. In this way the author's reaction, to make vitriolic fun at Trump's expense, seems true to a period in which, as I can testify, one was often dumbfounded by the depth of such monumental stupidity. It seems appropriate that the author's response to this monstrous man should be accompanied by his cartoon history of plagues, again displaying that form of resistance called humor.

Finally, if the book does not drown in these unpleasant subjects, it is because of the sensibility of the author and the wide knowledge he had of the connection between food and community (evident in his *A Plague Diner's Diary* at the end of the book), what today we call "food culture." For a few years members of this movement, the epicenter of which was Berkeley, California, where the author lived at the time, were called disparagingly "foodies," until gradually a deeper vein of meaning was revealed not only through community organizing (often led by chefs and enthusiastic diners), but in a philosophical shift, notable in the work of food writers from M.F.K. Fisher to Alice Waters to Mr. Harris. That is the deep connection we must all be grateful is generally accepted now between community, well being, and the ability of the earth to provide both pleasure and sustenance to all creatures.

With that I invite you to turn the page.

Susan Griffin
Berkeley, California
October, 2050

13

INTRODUCTION

W hat's to be made of a killer pathogen that pops up in the middle of our lives, disrupts everything, threatens everyone, and forces us underground like potatoes? This is not an alien invasion from outer space – though that may be happening too, according to recent military reports – but it's also not the kind of calamity anyone alive today has ever encountered. What to do? My answer in the spring of 2020 was simple: "Eat well, laugh, and keep a journal."

All current projects went on hold in March and, almost by default, Covid became the focus of my itchy fingers and anxious pens. I never imagined my plague year journal – text and art – would become a book. It just popped up, like the Covid-19 pandemic.

Much of the text material before you was posted on Facebook in earlier versions. Many of the drawings, too. I have used Facebook the way 19th century writers, most notably Honoré de Balzac, used a social media precursor called a *feuilleton*, an insert in publications that offered short and often humorous literary or political pieces and serializations of longer fictional works with their enticing cliffhangers. Balzac serialized many of his novels. So did Charles Dickens and Thomas Hardy in London magazines. Victorian serializations were all the rage in Europe and Great Britain.

One could say that my Covid projects and social media postings were a productive and pleasant way to pass the time while avoiding, to put it bluntly, death by plague. I was safe in my Berkeley bubble. As Giovanni Boccacio put it in *The*

Decameron, set in Florence during the Black Death plague in the 14th century. "Now, every person on earth has a natural right to maintain, preserve, and defend his life to the best of his ability." True enough. But "passing time" is not what artists, writers, photographers and the like do, especially amid wars and pandemics. I'm of the school that believes that in our work we find our true selves. Flannery O'Connor expresses it better: "I write because I don't know what I think until I read what I say." This is a writer's version of Descarte's more epistemological "I think, therefore I am." It's not about passing time – it's about capturing and preserving time and all its fleeting, sometimes dark, sometimes bright moments before they are forgotten. Pleasant is not a term I would use to describe the creative process, even during happier times.

The overall structure here is chronological, from the spring of 2020 to the summer of 2021. My focus has shifted back and forth between emerging themes that have become the book's four chapters: *My Pandemic Potato Clock*, the shock of the pandemic and isolation; *Plagues Then and Now*, a comparison of Covid with plagues past; *Masks and Miasma*, ancient and medieval theories of disease; and *Pandemics and Politics*, Covid's effect on our politics, with Donald Trump in the role of viral villain. Each chapter follows its own chronology, from 2020 through 2021.

In the final section of the book, *A Plague Diner's Diary*, I document my efforts to hold on to some form of gustatory and social pleasure during the pandemic. Along with the right of self-preservation that Boccaccio asserts is the right to enjoy life, as in our American "pursuit of happiness." In Berkeley, that means eating well. Easier said than done mid-pandemic, especially given the moral ambiguities of personal pleasure amid mass misery.

I hear more and more often these days the term "Covid time," and it is truly the strangest element of the pandemic, the shifting emotional color of time and a sense of lost time and the confusing gaps in one's memory of it. I have struggled mightily to maintain a true chronology in the book but have taken some liberties to honor the thematic sections. In this regard, some of the illustrations and text elements emerged before or after their respective places in the book's chronological flow. And I have expanded some of the shorter journal entries from early in 2020 with more current reflections. I am comforted by the mildly critical comments in a recent review of Daniel Defoe's *A Journal of the Plague Year* (1722), including, "somewhat chronological" and "frequent digressions and repetitions." I plead guilty to these quibbles and more, and console myself with the thought that a writer's faults should be modeled after those of their literary betters.

Our Covid-19 pandemic is not like political and natural disasters past – assassinations, terrorist attacks, earthquakes, hurricanes and the like. These happen on a particular day or over the course of several days. When over, and sometimes for the rest of our lives, we ask each other the question, "Where were you when such and such occurred?" We remember, of course, and report in vivid detail. But a pandemic, like a war, unfolds over a longer expanse of time with no clear start and stop dates. And the question is different: "What did you do during the pandemic besides cook, clean closets and hide?" My answer will be, and is now, "Read my book."

The colored illustrations throughout the book began as crude sketches in my journal where I figure out the coloring of the image and its relationship to the handwritten title and text. The finished illustrations based on these two sketches – *17th Century Plague Doctor* (left) and *Ancient Greek-Style White House Cleanse* (right) – are in the chapter Masks and Miasma.

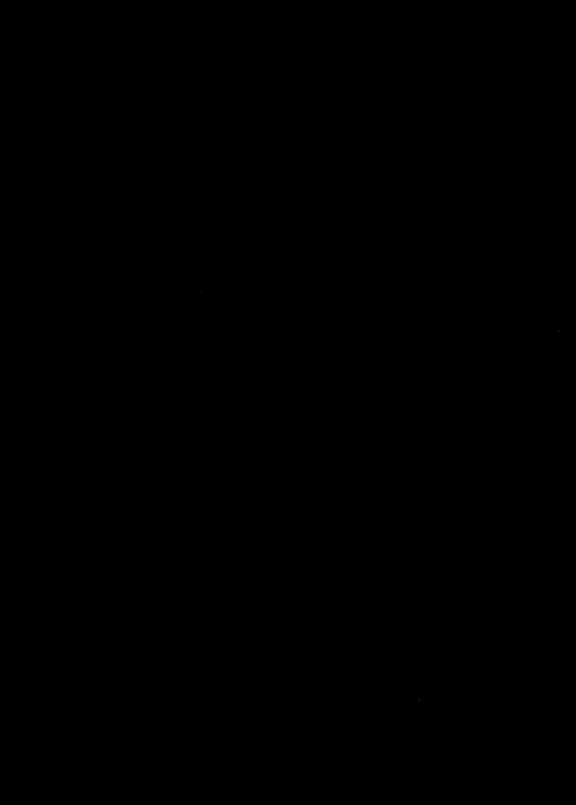

I | MY PANDEMIC POTATO CLOCK

As Gregor Samsa awoke one morning from uneasy dreams he found himself transformed in his bed into a gigantic insect.

— Franz Kafka
The Metamorphosis

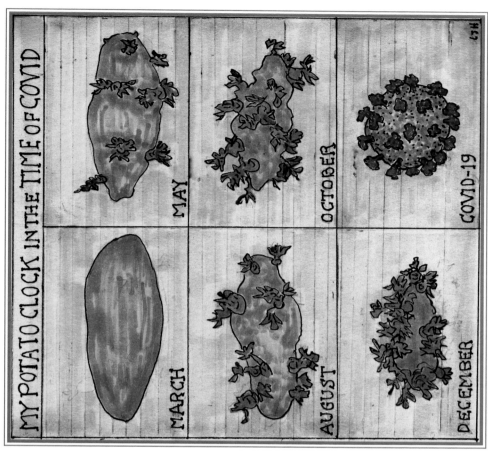

I put a russet potato on the window ledge in my kitchen in March of 2020 as the Covid virus took hold. By December, when I drew this image, it struck me that the potato was slowly morphing into the round pin cushion shape of the Covid-19 virus. The potato's green sprouts reminded me of the red spike proteins of Sars-CoV-2 and the potato's body was shrinking and rounding, reminding me as well of my body's plague year changes.

I n the year of our Lord 2020, when the Covid pandemic, raging wildfires in Northern California, hurricanes in the southeast, and Donald Trump's cartoonish anti-heroics in Washington D.C. transformed our lives into something out of a surreal dystopian thriller, I drew images, wrote texts, snapped photos and posted them on social media platforms. I didn't know what else to do.

My subject was a cascade of horrors: lonely streets and shuttered shops; hospitals filling up with coronavirus cases; burning forests and towns with thick smoky air that turned our visual world into impressionist paintings; restaurants and cafés imploding, many never to open again; educations and careers cancelled; social lives and love lives interrupted; with politicians and institutions inept in the face of it all.

New words and expressions crept into our daily discourse – shelter in place, lockdown, quarantine, shuttered, and social distance. They all added up to the same thing – life as we knew it was coming to a halt. And for how long nobody knew. Many Americans on the far political right saw it all as fake news or the End of Days. On the far left, there was outrage over unequal access to resources and medical care for minorities and immigrants. Locked down in Berkeley's middle realm (which leans decisively left), I had no idea what to make of it all as power politics and the pandemic panic seemed to merge. Aside from sending donations hither and yon, I felt impotent to do anything significant against the right or for the left. Had I fallen into a darkly absurd sitcom like South Park, or the plague-ravaged Thebes that Sophocles portrays in *Oedipus Rex?*

It was clear that time had suddenly been altered by a virus — an act of God as the ancients might see it. Call it panic time, or in this case, pan-*dem*-ic time. In the grip of this dark, confusing and lonely new time, I began hoarding food and essentials like everyone else: water, bagels, coffee, toilet paper, canned goods, hand wipes, masks (if you could find them) and a nutritionally rich and long shelf life root vegetable I love, but normally avoid (high carbs), the potato. I ended up with more russet potatoes than I could eat in a year, perhaps in a lifetime. I felt secure but, inevitably, fatter.

Stashing my potatoes in a cupboard, I put one of them on the windowsill above my kitchen sink to dry after scrubbing it, fully intending to cook it in the coming days. When the spud suddenly began to sprout, I left it on the sill, concluding it was not entirely fit to eat.

I couldn't avoid thinking about Van Gogh's famous *The Potato Eaters*, which could have just as easily been titled *The Coffee Drinkers*. Note that exactly half the painting is focused on coffee pouring (right) and half on potato eating (left). This is, in fact, a portrait of my bifurcated diet in Berkeley as Covid took hold, or so I feared — coffee by day; potatoes by night. To my eyes, Van Gogh's peasants even look like potatoes. This is an observation supported, according to documents at the Van Gogh Museum in Amsterdam, by the artist himself, who wrote to his brother in May of 1885 that the faces in the portrait were "…something like the colour of a really dusty potato, unpeeled of course."

The Potato Eaters. Vincent van Gogh (1885).

Documenting my potato: By May, the green sprouts were on full display and I took a photo and posted it on Facebook with a short explanatory text about my spud as a measure of time. Exposing this absurd concept on social media was prankish fun for me, and fun was in short supply. Thus began the ritual of photographing and posting my potato's changes over the course of a year. I had begun to think of my special tuber as a "potato clock," marking the progression of the pandemic as the months rolled by. It seems oddly appropriate that Covid would become symbolically embodied by a possibly poisonous, slowly rotting potato. After all, potatoes have been associated with famine (the Irish potato famine in the mid-19th century) and poverty (Van Gogh's *The Potato Eaters*). So why not a potato pandemic in the 21st century when lives were forced into survival mode? Aren't we all living underground "rotting in place" like potatoes?

A bit of research reveals that ancient time-keeping devices were hardly more sophisticated than my potato clock. There were sundials, of course, but also water clocks, candle clocks and incense clocks, all used to measure, however inaccurately, small increments of quotidian time. The impulse to know the time is part of the human condition. We are timekeepers. Some philosophers claim that we humans have actually created time, which is rather self-evident but confusing for non-philosophers like myself. Using the gradual deterioration of *Solanum tuberosum* as a time-keeping device may seem preposterous, but it adds a functional dimension to my fascination with a potato.

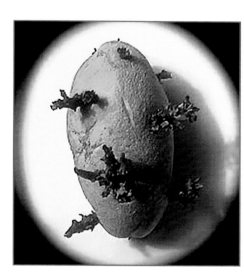

Potato update, August 2020: My potato clock ticks at variable rates. May's potato expressed my sense of time slowing down. I could see the potato sprout as if in slo-mo and the lonely days seemed long and uneventful – tedious. Then, with a burst of energy after a minor health scare, time seemed to speed up, becoming more generous. The potato's sprouts were spreading across its body and I began to spread out too, doing things I seldom had time for pre-Covid: cleaning out closets, organizing my desk and making mayonnaise from scratch. Now, in August, my potato clock has changed tempo again and Covid time feels neither slow nor fast, an extended duration, a timescape that may, like the pandemic itself, never end. Potato eternity. How would quantum physics or Dr. Fauci explain Covid time?

August 2020

Plague symptoms: Social isolation deepened after a hopeful but short-lived early summer lull in Covid cases and deaths. In response, my hygiene deteriorated to a level not common since Victorian times. Like many bachelors, I stopped shaving, let my hair grow and spent whole days in my robe and PJs in front of a TV or computer. When I dressed in the morning, if I dressed at all, I put on the same clothes I'd been wearing for a week. Living alone, socially isolated, would anyone care? Did I care? This was not a healthy frame of mind, and I noticed unpleasant symptoms. First, weight gain around the middle and aches and pains in joints and muscles. Then, lethargy and ennui. I was turning into a couch potato. A sad sack of potatoes.

Things got even worse. One day I noticed something growing on my upper lip, under my moustache – a tiny "thing". More potato identification and panic ensued as I watched the thing grow to the size of a tiny diamond. It hurt the way small unwanted things hurt, like paper cuts and splinters. Was my thing turning green like my potato's sprouts, indicating, perhaps, infection? No, thankfully not. Was it black or blue like a mini-plague bubo? No. Whatever it was, it brought out my Woody Allen hypochondria. Eventually I masked up and braved my skin doctor's office. She removed the thing, pronouncing it, a few days later, benign. Covid had turned a rather routine dermatological evaluation into a brush with death.

As my skin continued to sprout in the fall (another little thing grew on my eyelid), my hair was creeping inexorably closer to my shoulders. I observed in the mirror that my overall hair length seemed about the same, but how could this be? Because, I reasoned, my hairline was moving farther up my forehead. In other words, my scalp had shifted upwards, over and down the back of my head towards my shoulders, taking with it my thinning patch of gray. Plague logic.

Mr. Potato Head (left) and my pandemic potato clock (right), both photographed in October of 2020.

The Biochemistry of rot: During a pandemic one's mind runs to the grim. I began reading about the fraught biochemical phenomenon of the potato, a member of the deadly nightshade family, along with tomatoes and eggplant. Ironic that the birth process of potatoes – sprouting – produces its own protective chemicals – glycoalkaloids – that can, if ingested or inhaled in quantity as a gas, render potato eaters sick, even dead. The chemicals protect the potato from its predators (insects and rodents) but, ironically, not its human lovers. The potato's curious biology, the strange magic of its dangerous greenish flesh when damaged by excess exposure to light, co-existing with the deliciousness of the flesh when cooked, is more vivid to me now. My expectation, here in the winter of our discontent, is that my rotting potato will run itself into the ground along with the Covid pandemic sometime in mid-to-late 2021. If we are lucky. Is this Dicken's best of times *and* worst of times? No, far more the latter.

Speaking of Victorian Dickens, he missed London's last deadly bout of bubonic plague in the 17th century chronicled by Daniel Defoe in his *A Journal of the Plague Year* (1722), but he lived through and wrote about London's "Great Stink" in the mid-19th century. The term refers to the crisis of raw sewage dumped into the River Thames during one particularly hot summer (1858), creating not only a stink but also a breeding ground for cholera that killed tens of thousands. Drinking water in London came from the sewage-laced Thames, despite warnings from scientists and governmental authorities and the appearance of modern sanitary inventions. Many Londoners still thought, late into the 19th century, that "bad air" was the culprit, a vestige of the ancient and medieval miasma theory of disease.

A Potato year: It's now March, 2021, one year into my potato pandemic. I have adjusted. A veteran flâneur like me, locked down at home by a raging pandemic, morphs from a freewheeling urban caterpillar to a caged butterfly. Out of necessity, this solo lord of the manor becomes his own butler, in service only to himself. The daily tasks – flitting about his cage – are monotonous and seemingly endless, but not inconsequential.

Watching again *The Remains of the Day*, the film based on Kazuo Ishiguro's novel, there is a key scene where Stevens, the butler in service at Darlington Hall, takes a cloth and walks around the perimeter of the room's massive billiard table, wiping down its thick wooden frame. Lord Darlington has just been snookered in Darlington Hall's billiard room by a group of pro-Nazi sympathizers. Lost in thought, Stevens, played by Anthony Hopkins, removes smudges and dust from the polished wood, but also wipes away, in my interpretation, the grimy residue of Lord Darlington's pre-war betrayal he has just overheard. Stevens' life as a butler is a tightrope walk between denial and survival, amplified by his lord's betrayal and his own acquiescence.

Limited more or less to the boundaries of my gilded cage, like Stevens, and denied my usual rambles in Paris and Berkeley, I have embraced the lifestyle Covid has delivered: Overseeing a year-long remodeling project started before the pandemic, the keeping of a journal, endless cooking and solo eating, and the repetitive chores of a butler and staff. As both the lord of the manor and its loyal servant, I've made my peace with domestic service and a shuttered, albeit privileged, life. Again, as with Stevens, it's part denial, part survival—the pursuit of happiness in an unhappy time.

March 2021

Time to tidy up: The amount of housework one must accomplish living alone during a plague is daunting, both the daily chores – dish washing and laundry, sweeping and dusting, shopping and cooking – and the deeper deferred maintenance obligations of closet organization, cobweb removal, garden weeding, window cleaning, desk organizing and bookshelf arranging.

In love with real books, I spend a lot of time in my library as both lord and butler. I love my books, all of them, read and un-read. So what's with this current decluttering trend inspired by Marie Kondo in her 2014 bestseller, *The Life-Changing Magic of Tidying Up*, that suggests getting rid of books? Silly nonsense! To reduce a book's status to "clutter" is a crime against literature and the rich history of the library. But I do hate the affectation of domestic libraries shown in luxury home and design magazines, where shelved books are organized by size and spine color or wrapped in identical creamy dust jackets. I want the random colorful spines of my books lined up dead even along the edge of the shelves in thematic groupings. Mine is, after all, a working library, a resource for writer and reader; not an interior design focal point that turns the art of the book into a showy accessory. Let the books' colorful identities speak out on the shelves, but line them back up after use for a sense of order. Call me anal; call me, yes, a butt-ler.

The butler and his lord eat at the kitchen table nowadays. Still, the dining room gathers dust, fallout from the nearby construction zone, and it must be attended to. And when the delicate early 19th century farmhouse clock, mounted in an 18th century oak *vaisselier en bois* from Normandy, that sits against the wall across from the dining table, stops chiming, it requires a careful winding and adjustment of the hands. I trust my butler to take care of it. The French Morbier clock is constructed to chime on the hour, and then again three minutes after in case workers in the fields don't hear it the first time round. I read somewhere that the three-minute repetition is a reminder for Catholics to say a prayer. When I hear the repetition I smile, which is, I suppose, a form of prayer. The bells add a spiritual exclamation point to the sentence of lonely Covid days.

Potato update, June 2021: One day I began to clear my desk of clutter that had accumulated while working on a drawing. There, under a pile of sketches, was another clock, my potato clock. I must have left the incredible shrinking spud on the desk after drawing it last December. I note the body has shrunk to the size and texture of a very large irregular peanut, and the sprouts have turned a woody brown with only hints of green. It's as if the *élan vital* of the thing – its soul – has transmigrated. To another potato? To me?

Documenting the progress of the potato's decline has added, like my chiming clock and butler's chores, a sense of order to my Covid days. Boccaccio, in *The Decameron*, has one of his characters say, while explaining the required daily rituals to her young friends who have left plague-ravaged Florence with her to live in the country and tell bawdy stories in privileged safety, "Things that lack order will not last long." We are fortunate that our nightmare, though real, pales by comparison to that of Boccaccio's Florence. And I am fortunate that well past the one-year mark since the arrival of Covid-19, my aging at-risk flesh is alive and well, despite the "things" that sprout from it.

June 2021

II PLAGUES THEN AND NOW

Times of plague are always those in which the bestial and diabolical side of human nature gains the upper hand. Nor is it necessary to be superstitious, or even pious, to look upon great plagues as a conflict of the terrestrial forces with the development of mankind.

— Reinhold Niebuhr
The Nature and Destiny of Man

THE COLORFUL HISTORY OF PLAGUES, PANDEMICS & PESTILENCE

THE BLACK DEATH BUBONIC PLAGUE 1347	THE BLUE DEATH CHOLERA PANDEMIC 1826	THE BLACK & BLUE DEATH SPANISH FLU 1918	THE RED, WHITE & BLUE DEATH CORONA VIRUS 2020
BACTERIUM: YERSINIA PESTIS ORIGIN: CENTRAL/EAST ASIA SPREAD: INFECTED RODENT FLEAS	BACTERIUM: VIBRIO CHOLERA ORIGIN: INDIAN SUBCONTINENT SPREAD: FECAL WASTEWATER	VIRUS: H1N1 INFLUENZA A ORIGIN: POSSIBLY CHINA SPREAD: RESPIRATORY DROPLETS	VIRUS: SARS-COV-2 ORIGIN: CHINA SPREAD: RESPIRATORY DROPLETS
THERE HAVE BEEN VARIOUS NAMES FOR THIS DISEASE THAT WIPED OUT ONE THIRD OF EUROPE'S POPULATION IN THE MID-14th CENTURY. THE ORIGIN OF THE NAME IS UNCLEAR BUT MAY BE RELATED TO THE VICTIM'S SWOLLEN LYMPH NODES (BUBOES) THAT WOULD TURN BLACK.	THE CHOLERA PLAGUE HIT FRANCE HARD IN THE EARLY 1830s AND BECAME KNOWN AS "THE BLUE DEATH" BECAUSE INFECTED BODIES TURNED BLUE. OVER 20,000 DIED IN PARIS OUT OF A POPULATION OF 650,000. FRANCE HAD 100,000 DEATHS OUT OF A POPULATION OF 35,000,000.	THIS VIRULENT FORM OF THE FLU WOULD TURN ITS VICTIMS' FACES BLUE AND LIMBS BLACK. SPAIN WAS MISTAKENLY THOUGHT TO BE THE ORIGIN OF THE OUTBREAK BECAUSE ITS NEUTRAL STATUS DURING WW1 ALLOWED ITS PRESS TO PUBLISH HONEST REPORTS OF THE PANDEMIC'S SEVERITY.	OUR CURRENT PLAGUE MAY BECOME KNOWN AS "THE RED, WHITE AND BLUE DEATH" DUE TO THE POOR HANDLING OF THE PANDEMIC BY THE UNITED STATES GOVERNMENT. WITH NEW CASES NOW LEADING THE WORLD ON THE EVE OF ITS 2020 PRESIDENTIAL ELECTION. 11/28 LTH

Plague names are usually associated either with the place of origin or with a color based on the specific pathogen's effect on the body. As the presidential election approached, it was clear that Trump's "China virus" was really *his* virus by virtue of his failure to deal with it. You own what you deny. So, for this color-coded plague chart I rendered Covid-19 red, white and blue in honor of Trump's criminal mismanagement of America's Covid response.

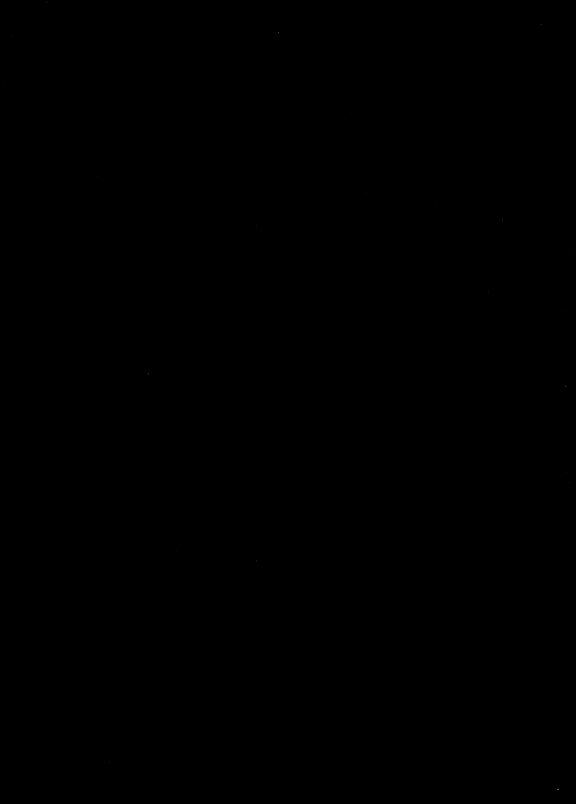

It felt so dark in Berkeley in the fall of 2020 as Covid surged back with a vengeance after the hopeful early summer respite. It was not yet common in the media or conversation to hear the pandemic referred to as a plague, a word which technically applies only to *the* plague – the various iterations of the bubonic bacterial plague that gave us the worst of these, the Black Death in the 14th century. It wiped out a third or more of Europe's population of 54 million souls. But our pandemic is not *just* a flu, as our president tried to minimize it. Influenza can be extremely deadly – witness the Spanish flu of 1918, a viral pandemic far more lethal than Covid. Nevertheless, Covid-19, *our* plague, is, was, and might be again nothing to sneeze at.

I've been reading up on the world's major historical scourges in books like *The Black Death* by Philip Ziegler and *Epidemics and Society* by Frank M. Snowden. One gains an appreciation for how really profound and culturally transformative all pandemics are, whatever they are called and whatever the pathogen responsible. Many advances in science and the arts, even the decline of feudalism and the rise of capitalism, are credited to the waves of bubonic plague in medieval Europe which took a heavy toll on the poor; elevated the wealthier segments of society and concentrated power in the state.

Ziegler points out that the Black Death created a whole new genre of literature from authors such as Giovanni Boccaccio, Geoffrey Chaucer, Daniel Defoe, Alessandro Manzoni and, more recently, Albert Camus who gave us a modern existentialist definition of the plague in his novel, *The Plague*: "But what does it mean, the plague? It's life, that's all." The Black Death also affected the iconography of European painting characterized by Memento mori motifs (skulls, hour glasses and other reminders of death) and the related Vanitas style of still lifes (add musical instruments, rotting fruit), as well as the Dance Macabre (Dance of Death) skeleton imagery that characterized Christian funerary art from Roman times through the Renaissance.

Plague art: Paintings of dying or dead plague victims surrounded by onlookers were common during this period. Joshua Loomis, in his book *Epidemics: The Impact of Germs and Their Power Over Humanity*, writes, "One of the most common images in plague art is that of victims in various stages of dying as other humans, saints, or angels try to help them."

The painting *St. Sebastian Interceding for the Plague-Stricken* (1497-1499) by Josse Lieferinxe shows St. Sebastian (center top), his body pierced by arrows, kneeling before God and pleading for humanity. The arrows represent, we are told, divine anger thrown down upon mankind for its sins, and the wounds of the arrows are said to represent bubonic buboes. Shakespeare would secularize this idea of fateful arrows in Hamlet, the "slings and arrows of outrageous fortune."

St. Sebastian Interceding for the Plague-Stricken. Josse Lieferinxe (1497-1499).

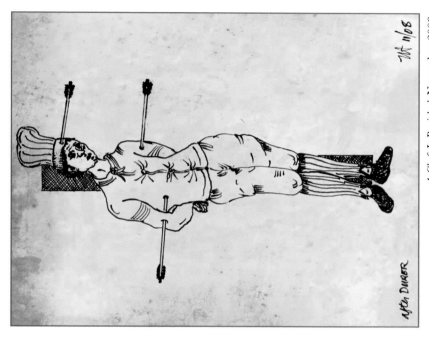

A Chef Is Punished. November 2008.

I didn't know the plague symbolism of Saint Sebastian's arrows, or his role as a Christian plague saint and protector, when I came across an engraving of the arrow-studded saint tied to a stake, *Saint Sebastian Bound to the Column* by Albrecht Dürer (1499). All I saw – perhaps failing to read the reproduction's descriptive text – was a possible cartoon appropriation of the saint as a chef punished for a culinary crime – stealing bacon from the royal larder. This was one in a series of "gastronomized" Renaissance and medieval drawings that appeared in my book, *Foodoodles* in 2010.

Joshua Loomis argues that the **Black Death** was not directly responsible for the darker preoccupations of medieval and Renaissance art. The themes of death, the soul, afterlife and Purgatory were already emerging in the decades before 1347 after changes in Catholic doctrine initiated by Pope Clement VI. The Black Death merely emphasized these elements in art's iconography.

Art historians are still studying the impact of the Spanish flu (and World War I) on the arts in Europe in the early 20th century – the emergence of Dada, Surrealism and abstraction. We won't know for years or decades (or even longer) how the Covid pandemic has affected our contemporary arts. I have a feeling, though, that the most dramatic impact will be in the world's poorest countries where the pandemic has caused the worst social and economic damage. The current globalization of the art market will only expand because of Covid.

Plague architecture: The effect of the Black Death on architecture was also dramatic, and major cathedrals were built and dedicated to plague saints like St. Sebastian and St. Roch. Visiting Venice in the summer of 2019, just months before Covid arrived in Europe, I stayed at the Bauer Palazzo Hotel on the Grand Canal opposite the Baroque basilica of Santa Maria della Salute, dedicated to plague victims. In Italian, *salute* means health or deliverance. The church's construction began in 1631, a votive offering to the Virgin Mary for the city's protection after the plague of 1630 took a third of its residents.

Sitting on the Bauer's elegant café terrace, I read up on the monumental Salute cathedral that loomed over me just a few hundred yards across the canal. I could understand the church's historical importance, but how could I know that shortly after my blissful stay in Venice a pandemic would emerge, and this grand cathedral would feel so much more powerful, and my encounter with it almost fated.

At the Bauer Palazzo Hotel in Venice in 2019. The Santa Maria della Salute cathedral looms behind me.

Cholera, art and Papa Sol: It has been noted by art historians that unlike the bubonic plague with its decorative polka-dotty buboes depicted in Christian art, cholera and its symptoms – watery green vomit and diarrhea – never became, thank God, a popular theme for painters. But in literary history, cholera has faired better. A friend who decided to spend Covid time reading Gabriel Garcia Márquez's *Love in the Time of Cholera*, sent me this passage from the book:

But when he began to wait for the answer to his first letter, his anguish was complicated by diarrhea and green vomit, he became disoriented and suffered from sudden fainting spells, and his mother was terrified because his condition did not resemble the turmoil of love so much as the devastation of cholera.

The speed with which cholera kills might also help explain its absence in art. Victims just don't last long enough to be painted. I know cholera first hand, or second hand actually, from my paternal grandfather who in 1902 contracted cholera in Vietnam while serving in the French Foreign Legion after his arrival in France from Poland. The outbreak was the fifth of seven cholera contagions to wash over the globe in the 19th and 20th centuries. Solomon Harris (né Azekowitch) had joined the Legion on his arrival in France in 1899 (the Legion would welcome almost anyone, even criminals, even Jews). He was sent first to North Africa to fight Arabs in the Sahara, and then to Tonkin, one of the French controlled provinces in what was then labeled Indochine (Indochina).

Sol Harris at home in L.A. in the 1950s.

In a short memoir dictated to his secretary in the 1950s, Sol describes his near-death experience in Indochina, not from the ubiquitous tigers and angry anti-colonials, but from cholera. During a mission in 1902, out from the port of Haiphong where he was stationed, his comrades were struck down:

Our company went on a march through a canyon on a hot, dry summer's day to a place called Hanjang I looked around suddenly and saw my comrades and officers alike falling down dead like flies. Each one of them was black, a terrible sight to see and half our company died on this march. The rest of us buried our comrades in this wistful canyon. I can hear the taps right now. In respect we stayed there that night. A few more died. It was cholera...

He continues his account back in Hanoi after the mission....

...we had servants to wash our clothes, cook our meals, clean our quarters and shine our shoes. We could demand anything we wanted to eat... But 75% of our soldiers were sick with fever and dying every day. One night talk to a Frenchman at breakfast and upon inquiring about him in the afternoon be told he was gone. I had the fever, too, and was sent to Hanoi Hospital. It is miraculous I came out alive...I don't recall how high my temperature was but I do remember I was shivering all the time. They put blankets on top of me, then threw me into bathtubs full of ice and this saved my life. I will always be grateful to the Sister who helped me to recover. To please her for the kind things she did I almost became a Catholic. I prayed and crossed myself and kneeled to please her.

After my grandfather recovered from cholera, he was discharged from the Legion and made his way to San Francisco aboard a sailing ship around Cape Horn. That was more than 100 years ago, and now I am writing a memoir of another plague.

Memento Mori: Covid Spikes and Cholera Tears. December 2020.

My last Covid drawing of 2020 was completed not long after the November election. Biden's victory certainly gave us a lift here in Berkeley, but the January 6 insurrection in DC brought us back to earth. It was evidently not going to be a happy new year. New was good enough.

We were still not out of the woods – politically or virally – and the vaccine's success story was not yet evident. The Stoic philosophers of antiquity thought "Memento mori" a healthy motto to live by – remember death. Today we say, "Gather ye rosebuds..." or, "Tick tock."

I must have had Damien Hirst's diamond-studded skull in mind — *For the Love of God* — when I drew my memento mori skull. I had seen Hirst's dead shark and other animals preserved in formaldehyde-filled tanks at his notorious Sotheby's auction in London in 2008. Then I saw his diamond-studded skull at the Tate Modern in 2012. I didn't really know what to make of it then — impressive, repulsive, obsessive, incisive? Today I'd say, all the above. The skull took $12,000,000 worth of diamonds to construct. That's putting money where your art is! He sold it for $100,000,000, though that may be an inflated number to boost his brand. I contrast Hirst's skull with Marcel Duchamp's worthless urinal, *Fountain*, 1917, presented for consideration at a New York art exhibition (and refused). How much would that modern art icon sell for today at auction — if it had not gone missing? $100,000,000 seems cheap.

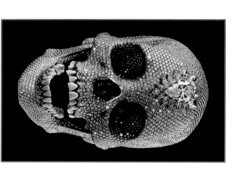

For The Love of God.
Damien Hirst (2007).

Damien's Hearse. 2015. Hirst's themes of money, art and death led me to consider his own end game and how, based on his outrageous formaldehyde-preserved animal vitrines, he could preserve himself as a traveling museum exhibit, displayed in a modified hearse parked in front of major art institutions.

INVASION OF THE PLANET SNATCHERS

A GLOBAL PANDEMIC SELFIE

A Global Pandemic Selfie. January 2021.

Covid's horrors have stimulated a year's worth of new work, so perhaps I should be grateful to it. Maybe Dickens was right after all – the best of times *and* the worst of times. In a sense this image does express a kind of respect for the power of this virus to "snatch" our world away from us. The drawing was posted on social media on January 7, a day after Trump tried to snatch our democracy away – an anthropomorphic view of our planet as a Covid-infected creature masked with the meme, "I Heart Covid." Our infected planet, according to this image, loves its new viral embodiment. Continents have become facial features, hair and a beard. Red spike proteins emerge from the ocean depths. It's a Covid selfie, taken from the virus's point of view, loving itself – our planet as the perfect host for Covid's nefarious intent.

III MASKS AND MIASMA

The miasma theory is an obsolete medical theory that held that diseases — such as cholera, chlamydia or the Black Death — were caused by a miasma (ancient Greek for "pollution"), a noxious form of "bad air", also known as night air. The theory held that deadly epidemics were caused by miasma, emanating from rotting organic matter.

— Wikipedia

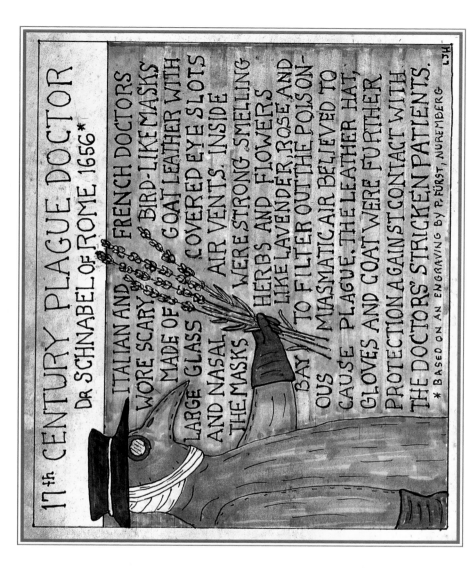

17th CENTURY PLAGUE DOCTOR
Dr SCHNABEL of ROME, 1656*

ITALIAN AND FRENCH DOCTORS WORE SCARY BIRD-LIKE MASKS MADE OF GOAT LEATHER WITH LARGE GLASS COVERED EYE SLOTS AND NASAL AIR VENTS. INSIDE THE MASKS WERE STRONG SMELLING HERBS AND FLOWERS LIKE LAVENDER, ROSE AND BAY TO FILTER OUT THE POISONOUS MIASMATIC AIR BELIEVED TO CAUSE PLAGUE. THE LEATHER HAT, GLOVES AND COAT WERE FURTHER PROTECTION AGAINST CONTACT WITH THE DOCTOR'S STRICKEN PATIENTS.

* BASED ON AN ENGRAVING BY P. FÜRST, NUREMBERG

51

My plague doctor is based on Paulus Fürst's satirical 1656 engraving titled "Doctor Schnabel von Rom" or "Doctor Beaky from Rome". Fürst's image was copied from an illustration by the German engraver Gerhart Altzenbach. The medieval plague doctor and his costume became a popular presence on the stages of commedia dell'arte theater.

PART 7

DRUG-FREE GUIDE TO DEFEATING YOUR DEPRESSION

Chapter 81

The tragic truth about antidepressants

If you're suffering from depression, the promise of relief in the form of a little pill can feel like a lifeline. So the fact that antidepressants have few—if any—real benefits is, well...*depressing*.

You're better off passing on the SSRIs—and using natural solutions instead.

That's the conclusion published last month in the British Medical Journal. And it's consistent with views I have presented before in Insiders' Cures. My practice in forensic medicine backs it up too. I've seen case after case of depressed patients committing suicide... *after they start taking "antidepressant" drugs.*

Making matters worse, it's not that antidepressants don't do anything—it's just that they do the wrong thing. The newer antidepressant drugs act as selective serotonin reuptake inhibitors (SSRIs). They artificially raise levels of serotonin in the brain by preventing its normal re-uptake into nerve cells after it's released into nerve pathways.

This is believed to help depression symptoms. And it does...but not the symptoms that need to be improved.

In my forensic medicine practice, I saw case after case of chronically depressed patients with suicidal thoughts. But they were too depressed to take action and do anything about it. *Until they got their dose of SSRIs, that is.* Once the drugs kicked in, the patients still had their suicidal thoughts, and now they had the energy to act on them. The results were tragic.

Even more tragic is that some mentally troubled, depressed patients have thoughts about harming others as well. Disturbing new analysis indicates many of the recent violent tragedies grabbing the headlines may be the result of antidepressants.

That's because depression has a built-in self-protection. It causes people to turn inward, close themselves off, and they lack the energy to carry out actions. Instead they just endlessly think these thoughts, many of them negative. Psychiatrists call this *thought substitution.* So even if people have thought of hurting themselves or others, they often don't have the energy or ability to do it.

Now give the depressed person Prozac. You haven't changed anything about the real causes of the depression. But, suddenly, the depressed person's brain is flooded with serotonin. And now they finally have the energy to act.

I'll leave it to statisticians to debate whether SSRIs cause suicide in depressed patients. But as a physician, the evidence in real cases of suffering human beings is all too obvious.

Still, serotonin is not just a loaded gun waiting to go off. And while I don't recommend artificially manipulating your serotonin levels as a treatment for any disease, I can tell you that there are natural approaches that really work. They help the body naturally restore its own proper levels of serotonin, acetylcholine, and other neurotransmitters. And that makes for a healthy mind and body.

I'll tell you more about these natural depression helpers in a minute. But first…

Other ways antidepressants can kill you

Beyond suicide, antidepressants have many other scientifically proven side effects. The most dangerous of these include:

Birth defects. The CDC recently conducted a study of over 27,000 mothers of children with birth defects. The researchers found that the women who took Prozac and Paxil during their first trimester of pregnancy, or the month before they became pregnant, were substantially more likely to have children with significant birth defects.

Specifically, they found that these poor children had a two to 3.5 times greater risk of obstructed blood flow from their heart to their lungs, holes in their heart walls, missing pieces of their brains and skulls, and irregularly shaped skulls. Abdominal wall defects were also a possibility, although the evidence wasn't as strong.

This isn't the first study linking birth defects to antidepressants, but it's one of the largest and most definitive.

Bleeding in the skull. A recent study of about 4 million South Koreans found that those who combined any kind of antidepressant with NSAID painkillers like aspirin or ibuprofen had a staggering 60% chance of bleeding inside their skull. This can lead to strokes, brain damage, or even death.

And another study of 2,500 people with an average age of 59 found that these bleeds could start as late as <u>four years</u> after someone first took an antidepressant. Unlike the Korean study, this study found that antidepressants alone could cause brain bleeding, and SSRIs posed the biggest risk. The researchers concluded that doctors should be careful about prescribing SSRIs—especially to older people.

Breast cancer. Research shows that 70% of cancerous breast tumors increase in size when estrogen levels rise. And Paxil has been found to have an estrogen-like effect on the body. So it's certainly not a leap to assume that taking Paxil can increase a woman's risk of breast cancer.

And since SSRIs have the same basic mechanism of action, it's a (un) safe bet Prozac, Zoloft, Lexapro, and Celexa can escalate your risk of breast cancer just like Paxil does.

Heart problems. In 2013, I reported on research showing that the SSRIs Celexa and Lexapro are linked to dangerous heart rhythm abnormalities. And we've known for decades that older types of antidepressants called tricyclics (Norpramin is the most common brand) can cause sudden cardiac deaths.

Fortunately, you don't see many prescriptions for tricyclics these days. But even though the FDA issued a warning about Celexa's heart issues in 2011, many uniformed doctors still encourage their patients to take it.

Liver damage. In an exhaustive study, French researchers found 158 different scientific reports since 1965 that showed that up to 3% of people who took antidepressants had signs of liver damage.

The researchers discovered that this damage could potentially begin within a few days of first taking a wide variety of antidepressants. And older people appear to be most vulnerable—no matter what dosage they took.

Mental health problems. Ironically, the very drugs designed to alleviate one mental condition may actually create more mental conditions.

There is evidence linking antidepressant use to anxiety psychosis and mania. And, as I wrote in an October 2014 Daily Dispatch ("Antidepressant drug shuts down brain connectivity within three hours"), research shows that just a single dose of an SSRI can reduce connectivity in the brain. Meaning these drugs could create an emotionally blunted, lobotomy-like effect in some people.

Antidepressants on the rise

Why are prescriptions for antidepressants going up and up, while the people taking them continue slipping down into their depression or suffer even more serious physical side effects as discussed above?

Some psychiatrists claim it's because of a small, but appropriate, increase in the length of treatment—not the number of patients being treated. That is, patients are being kept on the drug longer.

But why keep people on the same tired medication if it's not working?

The real issue is that too many people are being treated for something that's just a normal part of life—not a disease in need of a pharmaceutical cure. The current definition of clinical depression is two weeks of "low mood". I can think of a number of people whose moods were low for a couple weeks after the last election. But I wouldn't call it a disease—and I certainly wouldn't want to medicate it away!

A more serious mental illness is being so delusional that you can't recognize when bad and sad things are happening in reality—and that's much worse than two weeks of "low mood".

But some parties have reason to be in a good mood about the overuse of antidepressants. **Three-quarters of psychiatrists who write the definitions of depression used in the psychiatric manual have links to drug companies.** So they have good motivation to put people on prescriptions and abandon more time-intensive—but effective—mental health treatments! (Think psychoanalysis, talk therapy, and even spiritual approaches.)

Depression may be the perfect condition for the drug industry: Incurable, common, long-term (even with these so-called "treatments"), and involving multiple medications. Some experts say contemporary psychiatry's relationship with the drug industry has created a pharmaceutical mindset to treat mental illness.

But the National Institute for Health and Clinical Excellence does not even support the use of antidepressants for mild depression. Instead it favors psychological talk-based therapies.

Of course, the government industrial-insurance complex doesn't want to pay health professionals for the time it takes to really help patients. Instead they push the quick treatment—the few seconds it takes to scribble on a prescription pad (often with the name of the drug also advertised at the top).

Perhaps *that's* why antidepressant prescriptions increased by almost 10 percent in 2011.

Or perhaps it's because 25 to 60 percent of SSRI prescriptions are written for conditions that have nothing to do with depression.

The list of health issues SSRIs are supposedly able to treat is staggering. Arthritis, fibromyalgia, nerve pain, irritable bowel syndrome, autism… even premature ejaculation.

Based on this evidence, is it any wonder why so many people take antidepressants these days? Busy, distracted doctors, prodded by big pharma, are treating these drugs like the "tonics" that used to be sold by snake-oil salesmen—designed to cure anything that ails you.

The upside of being down

Occasional "low mood" may simply be a fact of life. In fact, research shows that mildly depressed people are actually better at assessing and dealing with life's circumstances. Sometimes low mood is just our way of seeing that all is not well, and that we need to protect ourselves.

Shakespeare was no stranger to low mood when he wrote the character of Hamlet. When Hamlet perceives that "something is rotten in the state of Denmark," it leads to his famous soliloquy: "To be, or not to be—that is the question…whether to suffer the slings and arrows of outrageous fortune, or take arms against a sea of troubles, and by opposing them, end them."

Sounds like an appropriate response to a dangerous situation, doesn't it? To most of us anyway… But not to some ever-alert psychiatrists, who have used that soliloquy to diagnose Hamlet as depressed.

Nature's answer to depression

While antidepressant drugs may be worse than worthless for many or most people, many natural approaches can enhance brain, mind, and mood. In fact, there are three nutrients in particular that have been proven in hundreds of scientific studies to help fight depression, but also many, if not all of the conditions antidepressants are currently being prescribed to help.

By incorporating this Triple Nutrient Cure into your daily routine, and thereby overcoming a possible deficiency within your body, you could begin to turn the tides on depression for good.

Here are the specific recommendations for the Triple Nutrient Cure…

1. **Vitamin D**. 10,000 IU a day.

I recommend having your vitamin D levels checked every 12 months through a routine blood test. Your doctor will order the test during your annual check-up. But between visits, and especially at the end of a long, dark winter like this one, you should keep an eye out for 10 signs you may have a vitamin D deficiency.

We know vitamin D helps produce adequate levels of serotonin, a critical neurotransmitter in the brain that produces feelings of well-being. And many solid, independent studies link low vitamin D levels with depression.

Evidence reveals low vitamin D with increased anxiety, which frequently accompanies depression. Aside from clinical conditions like anxiety or depression, vitamin D's effect on serotonin can impact mood in anybody. So if your mood is off, it may be a sign of vitamin D deficiency.

And it's not just deficiencies either. Research published in Psychosomatic Medicine revealed "vitamin D supplementation may be effective for reducing depressive symptoms in patients with clinically significant depression."

When researchers tested vitamin D supplementation against depressive symptoms of 441 overweight subjects, they saw a relation between serum levels of vitamin D and symptoms of depression. Supplementation with high doses of vitamin D seems to alleviate these symptoms.

And for severe mental disorders such as bipolar disorder, schizophrenia, and impulsive behavior, research has shown vitamin D along with omega-3 fatty acids may help prevent and modulate the severity of brain dysfunction.

And that's only the beginning. Researchers have shown congestive heart failure, high blood pressure, chronic pain, muscle weakness, and respiratory illnesses can all be linked to low levels of vitamin D.

2. B vitamins.

I recommend a high-quality B vitamin complex that contains at least 200 mcg of folate, 50 mg of B6, 12 mcg of B12, 50 mg of B2, and 50 mg of choline.

Even though you find B12 in foods like eggs, red meat, and milk.

These are all the things we've been told we should avoid. So millions of men and women think they are following doctor's orders by limiting eggs, red meat, and dairy but they then go on to develop a B12 deficiency. And they don't even realize it because most doctors don't test B12 levels unless there's a problem.

But it's a huge problem for your brain, mood, and overall neurological health.

B vitamins offer many brain benefits — including preventing and reversing dementia and age-associated brain changes. In fact, a new study shows brain levels of vitamin B12 do decrease with age, but they are prematurely low in people with autism spectrum disorder and schizophrenia.

In fact, B vitamins are so important to brain function, they're called "neurovitamins" in Europe.

The *American Journal of Clinical Nutrition* reported that in elderly adults, high total intakes of vitamin B6 and B12 are protective against depressive symptoms.

And the *Journal of Psychopharmacology* found low B12 status is a great indicator of major depression, but also oral doses of both folic acid and vitamin B12 should be tried to improve the treatment and outcome in depression.

3. Omega-3 fatty acids. 1-2 grams of high-quality fish oil daily.

Many experts consider omega-3s one of the keys to the Mediterranean Diet. And a number of studies link the Mediterranean diet with mental health benefits. In fact, recent studies show adults who follow the Mediterranean Diet most closely for four to five years had a 40 to 60 percent reduced risk of depression.

Further, research published in the *Journal of Clinical Psychiatry* found a direct correlation between the severity of anxiety and levels of EPA and DHA levels within the body. The lower, the more severe.

And when one study compared omega-3's oils directly to

antidepressant—reviewers wrote, "our review finds comparable benefit."

And this is an all-natural treatment that has been tested against antidepressants—readily available to you at a fraction of the cost.

The Triple Nutrient Cure is powerful because each component supports the brain and keeps it healthy...which fights depression at the root of the cause. And that is something none of the pharmaceutical antidepressants can do.

Chapter 82

Feed your brain: What you should—and shouldn't—eat for better mental health

Want to improve your mental health? Start by improving your diet.

American psychiatrists are finally beginning to take note of what I've been telling you all along: Your brain needs nutrients just like your body does.

And what's the best way to get all those particular nutrients? From food.

In fact, a recent analysis of 17 different studies found that in nearly half of the studies, dietary changes significantly improved depression.

And during an annual meeting of the American Psychiatric Association, there was an entire session on the best foods to support mental health. Not surprisingly, those foods did not include processed junk, sugary foods, or white bread and pasta.

Let's take a look at what else you should—*and shouldn't*—be eating to fight depression and anxiety…and improve your overall mental health and mood.

5 foods you might not expect to boost your mood

Meat. We now know when it comes to eating meat, what we have been told by the government for decades is just flat-out wrong. We actually need to eat more—not less—of this food for both physical and mental health. In fact, the researchers who conducted the meta-analysis of 17 studies I mentioned above specifically recommended diets that <u>did not</u> reduce red meat or cholesterol intake.

Meat is a nutrient-dense source of minerals and vitamins A, B, and D. And of course, it's an excellent source of protein.

As I've reported before, B vitamins are so important to brain function, they're called "neurovitamins" in Europe. And there are scores of studies showing that vitamin D can help reduce depression and lower your risk of Alzheimer's disease.

Meat is also a good source of cholesterol and fat. The omega-3s in cholesterol and fat actually help build and support the structure of brain and nerve cell membranes (not to mention every other tissue cell in the body).

Bottom line: Every one of us needs cholesterol and fat for healthy brains and nerves. And one of the best sources of both of these nutrients is meat. While plants like chia and flax contain some omega-3s, they're not the same brain-building type that are found in meat.

There are, of course, many ethical problems with industrial meat production. Opt for organic, grass-fed beef instead of corn-fed (almost all corn grown in the U.S. is GMO now). These more natural agricultural practices are much less abusive to animals, and also result in much healthier foods.

Eggs. We have been ridiculously advised by the government to avoid this perfect food. But like meat, eggs are a good source of cholesterol and other nutrients, making them one of the best foods for the brain.

Making an omelet in the morning with some red peppers, for example, is a tasty and healthy brain treat. (The color of the pepper is a clue to its nutrient quality. The presence of bright red, orange, yellow, green, blue, and purple in natural foods is a sign that they're packed with vitamins, carotenoids, anthocyanins, flavonoids, and other valuable phytonutrients.)

As with meat, look for eggs from humanely raised animals. That means free-range and organic (which ensures the chickens aren't given antibiotics).

Oysters, clams, and other seafood. When it comes to nutritional value per ounce, few foods measure up to bivalves like oysters and clams. A half-dozen oysters on the half-shell provide 272 percent of the daily intake of vitamin B12, and 509 percent of daily zinc.

Zinc has been shown in a variety of studies to be critical for memory and cognition—especially as we age.

Bivalves and other seafood are also leading sources of vitamin D and omega-3s. And they're rich in chromium and iodine—two minerals important for brain function. The omega-3s in seafood also help support the production of a chemical called brain-derived neurotropic factor (BDNF). BDNF plays a role in the survival and growth of neurons. Research has also shown that, in patients suffering from depression, anxiety, and mood disorders, higher BDNF levels result in less severe symptoms.

Liver and organ meats. These foods also get a bad rap, but nothing is more nutritious. Predatory animals on the hunt always go for the organ meats first, since they are the densest sources of vitamins and minerals—literally storing them up for the rest of the body.

Not a fan of liver or other organs? You can disguise the taste and texture by adding them to delicious vegetable stews, or many different varieties of chili con carne.

Nuts. Like meat and eggs, nuts were also once "off limits" because they're considered high-fat treats. But that kind of thinking is "nuts," according to the science. A handful of tree nuts (almonds, cashews, pistachios, walnuts) can help ward off diabetes, heart disease, and obesity. And nuts improve brain health.

Nuts are full of bioavailable brain-boosting minerals like manganese and selenium. Not to mention protein, omega-3s, and vitamin E—which has tremendous brain benefits.

In fact, one study showed that adding nuts to a Mediterranean diet resulted in overall improvements in depression and mental health.

Until recently, researchers assumed that these benefits only came with relatively expensive tree nuts. But new research shows that peanuts (which grow in the ground) are just as healthy at much less cost. (Peanut butter did <u>not</u> have the same health benefits, probably due to the addition of sugars and other added ingredients.)

Finally, the information on the food labels for nuts is all wrong when it comes to calorie counts. One study showed that almonds actually have 25 percent *fewer* calories than thought. And there's speculation that calorie counts could be significantly lower for other nuts as well.

Sidestep these two mental-health minefields.

Vegetarian or vegan diets. Of course, we all know that plants have an important role in a balanced diet. But, as I have uncovered in the past, strictly plant-based diets are not healthier for body or brain.

B-vitamin deficiency is commonly associated with vegetarian diets and causes development delays in children and brain atrophy in adults. And some research shows a vegetarian diet is associated with increased anxiety and depression.

Plants just can't provide enough healthy fats, minerals, and vitamins that are crucial for good mental health. And, unlike meat and seafood, they also don't have the full range and variety of amino acids that are needed in proteins.

Gluten. Most of the health, metabolic, and weight problems associated with grains come from their high carbohydrate content. But the gluten protein found in wheat and other grains can also be a culprit.

We already know that gluten can cause allergic reactions, including celiac disease, in some people. And now there's evidence that it may be a factor in psychosis.

A large clinical trial demonstrated that people diagnosed with schizophrenia have significantly elevated anti-gliadin antibodies (gliadin is a component of gluten). The researchers found that over 23 percent of schizophrenic patients have high anti-gliadin antibodies, compared with only 3 percent of controls.

In one case, an underweight but otherwise healthy 37-year-old woman became paranoid and psychotic over a period of a year. She entered into the "downward spiral" of mental illness, losing her job, home, family, and friends. Numerous psychiatric drugs were useless.

But after only three months of a gluten-free diet, her mental condition became stable.

Later, she consumed just one gluten-heavy meal. She ended up back in the hospital. But when she went back to a gluten-free diet, she resumed normal mental health—without any drugs.

A growing amount of research also shows that gluten may influence the microbiome—the "good" bacteria in your gut. In addition to controlling digestion, the microbiome appears to be important for mental health.

Irritable bowel syndrome (IBS), is also influenced by the microbiome (and vice versa). And IBS is associated with anxiety and depression. That's because the digestive process may involve conversion of the amino acid tryptophan to serotonin—powerful neurotransmitter that influences depression and other moods.

Many of the bacteria of the microbiome actually make their own neurotransmitters, which communicate with the vagus nerve. The vagus nerve originates in the brain, as one of the twelve cranial nerves, and travels throughout the internal organs and gastrointestinal tract. Scientists don't yet know what the gut is saying to our vagus nerve, but they think the brain is listening.

If you do decide to try a gluten-free diet, remember that many non-grain-based foods are naturally gluten-free. There are also a growing number of delicious and nutritious gluten-free breads and baked goods. I have personally inspected, and highly recommend, Aleia's Gluten Free Foods. To find a store near you that sells these healthy goodies, or to buy them online, visit www.aleias.com.

In mental health, as in virtually all other aspects of health, diet is the best option we have for health promotion and disease prevention.

Chapter 83

Eat more of these foods to improve mental health

A good diet is a basic tenet of good physical health. And it's a basic tenet of good *mental* health as well. In fact, as I'll explain in a moment, you can improve your depression risk by up to 60 percent by making a few simple changes to your diet.

It seems American psychiatrists are *finally* starting to take note of the all the good research on nutrition and mental health. In fact, at an American Psychiatric Association's (APA) annual meeting, Dr. Drew Ramsey, assistant clinical professor of Psychiatry at Columbia University College of Physicians & Surgeons, led a session about the best foods to support mental health was included.

We all know a good diet supports body and brain function. And the body and mind are connected. So it makes perfect sense the foods that support good physical health would also support good mental health.

According to Dr. Ramsey, "Food is a very effective and underutilized intervention in mental health." He continued, "…patients have more resilient brains by using whole foods…by getting off processed foods, off white carbohydrates, and off certain vegetable oils."

Of course, you would never hear this advice from the mainstream. The only "solution" they offer patients struggling with depression is to take an antidepressant drug. But this "solution" does very little to actually help the patient—and all too often it causes more harm than good.

Plus, remember the infamous Harvard study on depression from 2002? In that study, researchers found neither SSRI drugs nor dietary supplements worked better than placebo for depression. But the "placebo" received by everyone in the study was 14 hours of counseling by a skilled mental health professional…and they *did* experience some improvements.

That Harvard study always reminds me that talking and listening to the patient is more effective than handing out any pill, whether drugs or supplements. And you don't have to conduct formal psychoanalysis either. Apparently just talking about anything important to the patient helps.

In fact, in another recent study, just *discussing diet* with a counselor for six hours over the course of two years decreased depression scores by 40 percent in elderly patients. Thankfully, many experts are beginning to recognize the psychiatry of food.

A paper published in the British journal **Lancet Psychiatry** attested: "Although the determinants of mental health are complex, the emerging and compelling evidence for nutrition as a crucial factor in the high prevalence and incidence of mental disorders suggests that diet is as important to psychiatry as it is to cardiology, endocrinology, and gastroenterology."

Plus, a 2014 meta-analysis of clinical trials showed dietary interventions improved depression comparable to antidepressant drugs in half the studies.

Now, back to the APA session…

Dr. Ramsey and his co-presenter took a stab at explaining human biology and evolutionary biology to support the importance of diet to mental health.

They made a good point about the importance of seafood to the human brain. They said the earliest human ancestors in the African Rift Valley lived close enough to the seacoast to have reliable access to seafood.

Of course, early modern humans emerged during the Ice Age on the northwest coast of Europe, where they clearly took advantage of seafood. In fact, as recently as 100 years ago, anthropologists observed healthy indigenous peoples on the northwest coast of North America who didn't farm at all. They gleaned most of their nutrition from marine foods such as fish and seafood.

Indeed, oysters, and other mollusks are very ancient marine creatures.

And they're very high in nutrients, including B vitamins, which are commonly deficient in vegan or vegetarian diets. The human brain needs vitamin B12 for neurotransmitter functions. It also supports healthy myelin, which insulates nerve endings.

Of course, oysters and other kinds of seafood also provide abundant natural cholesterol and omega-3 fatty acids for our brains, which are composed of 60 percent fats.

Humans only began cultivating and consuming agricultural products—such as grains, legumes (beans), and dairy—about 6,000 to 10,000 years ago. The history books call this an advancement of civilization. But I would disagree. Archaeologists found evidence that human health and nutritional status *declined* and growth became stunted among populations who adopted agricultural foods compared to hunter-gatherer ancestors.

Clearly, the government's advice to cut out cholesterol and fats from the diet was a disaster for our health—both physical and mental. And mainstream medicine still pushes the disastrous cholesterol-lowering drugs, which poison normal metabolism.

Plus, many Americans—when they tried to follow the government's advice to cut fats and cholesterol—ended up with a diets filled with processed grains and sugars, which lack nutritional value.

Also, many of the people who went to the extreme and tried to follow a vegan/vegetarian diet ended up following a high-carb diet—which usually amounts to a high-sugar diet and is unhealthy for all the same reasons. Indeed, pregnant women who follow vegetarian diets run the same risk of suffering from anxiety as those women who follow high-sugar diets.

I *do* respect ethical concerns about the treatment of animals. But it's hard to make the case for vegan/vegetarian diets based on that ethical argument alone. The human body simply needs the bioavailable nutrients found in meat and seafood.

A number of studies link the Mediterranean diet—high in fish, olive oil, nuts, and wine—with mental health benefits. In fact, recent studies show adults who follow the Mediterranean Diet most closely for four to five years had a 40 to 60 percent reduced risk of depression.

Of course, evidence shows the Mediterranean diet benefits the heart and circulatory system as well. And it improves mental focus, energy, and self-confidence. Indeed, a healthy diet is the first step in this virtuous cycle.

My colleague Don McCown is the Director of the Center for Contemplative Studies at West Chester University of Pennsylvania. He just visited with me in New England to work on our next book together. He shared a quip about what causes mental health and illness, "It's more about what's out there, than what's in here".

In other words, you can accomplish a great deal by understanding interpersonal and social factors without having to conduct abstract internal psychoanalysis. Plus, what you put "in there" (in your body) is an important factor too.

Chapter 84

Support serotonin naturally

Antidepressant drugs known as SSRIs (selective serotonin reuptake inhibitors) only work for about one in seven depressed patients. And that *one* patient out of seven probably only feels better because of a placebo effect.

Fortunately, you *do* have many natural treatment options if you suffer from depression. There are some encouraging findings about the role of omega-3 fatty acids (EPA and DHA) and vitamin D for improving the health of both the brain and the mind.

Unlike conventional medicine, in the world of natural medicine, there is no real distinction between brain and cognitive health versus emotion, mood and mental health. In other words, there is no artificial, imaginary barrier between "neurological" or "cognitive" disorders, thought of as brain conditions…and "psychiatric" disorders, thought of as mental conditions. Brain, mind and mood all function together naturally.

In a paper published in the *FASEB* journal (Federation of American Societies for Experimental Biology), researchers made four excellent points.

First, the researchers recognized the connection between "cognitive" and "psychiatric" disorders. And they theorized if a treatment works for "cognitive" disorders, it should also work for "psychiatric" disorders.

Second, they pointed to the wealth of previous research that shows omega-3 essential fatty acids (found in marine or fish oils) and vitamin D improve brain function.

Third, they theorized that omega-3s and vitamin D should then also work for "psychiatric" disorders like depression. The researchers even highlighted a "mechanism of action" that could help explain how and why omega-3s and vitamin D support mental health.

A mechanism of action explains *how* something works in the body. And this point is important because scientists in the 21st century can't just accept that a treatment works. They need to know *how* and *why* it works.

Fourth, the researchers brought up the very good point that the brain needs essential fatty acids and vitamin D to support normal production of serotonin. But drugs like SSRIs act by "blocking" the reuptake of serotonin back into brain cells.

As I've said before, drugs that chemically "block" normal metabolic processes are a bad bet. Whether it's a statin drug that "blocks" normal cholesterol. Or a bone density drug that "blocks" and kills normal bone cells. Or an SSRI that blocks the reuptake of serotonin. Using drugs that "block" normal functions don't follow a normal or natural path to good health. "Blockers" belong on a football team, but not in your body. I'm much more inclined to recommend nutrients that support normal functions so the body can preserve or restore normal health.

So back to the new research at hand...

First, let's take a look at vitamin D. As the researchers pointed out, vitamin D acts more like a hormone than a simple nutrient in the body. Also, it regulates the conversion of the essential amino acid tryptophan into serotonin.

Of course, serotonin isn't the only important neurotransmitter in the brain. But it *does* influence a wide range of cognitive functions and behavior. Including mood, decision-making, social behavior, impulsive behavior, and social decision-making.

Plus, research links many clinical conditions to disordered serotonin activity, including from autism (ASD), attention deficit hyperactivity disorder (ADHD), bipolar disorder, depression, and schizophrenia.

Next, let's look at essential fatty acids.

One type of fatty acid called eicosapentaenoic acid (EPA) facilitates serotonin release from brain cells into synapses between cells. EPA appears to act through its anti-inflammatory properties. It reduces inflammatory molecules in the brain called E2 prostaglandins. These inflammatory prostaglandins negatively impact serotonin in brain cells. They also block the release of serotonin into the synapses between cells.

Another type of fatty acid called docosahexaenoic (DHA) influences serotonin receptors. It makes the receptors more accessible by increasing cell membrane fluidity.

Now, how do vitamin D and essential fatty acids work *together*?

Your body converts vitamin D into a steroid hormone that regulates more than 1,000 different gene pathways, many in the brain. Then, the essential fatty acids interact with these pathways in the brain, including the serotonin pathway. These pathways are important for mood, cognition and decision-making.

The problem is, most people don't get enough fatty acids and vitamin D into their diets. Most people don't eat enough fish, which is the best source of omega-3 fatty acids such as EPA and DHA. Of course, your skin will produce plenty of vitamin D on its own if exposed to enough sunlight. But during fall and winter months, the sun isn't strong enough to activate vitamin D on the skin.

I suggest supplementation. Improving your intake of vitamin D, EPA and DHA with supplementation will naturally support serotonin activity in the brain. It will also help prevent and improve depression and other cognitive functions. The one thing it *won't* do is cause adverse side effects. The only "side effects" it will cause are other proven health benefits provided by these essential nutrients.

You can find EPA and DHA in high-quality fish oil supplements. But you want to make sure the manufacturer prepares the fish oil supplements according to specific procedures.

When it comes to vitamin D, I recommend everyone take 5,000 IU per day year-round. It's especially important during fall and winter months. You can find vitamin D in an easy-to-use liquid form, together with the carotenoid antioxidant powerhouse astaxanthin.

Chapter 85

Popular drugs help only 1 in 7 patients

Doctors dole out antidepressants far too easily. To far too many people. And for far too long. Plus, few antidepressants, if any, truly benefit their patients.

I've hounded this point many times before. And now, it seems I'm not the only doctor who is unafraid to speak the truth about these drugs. In the *British Medical Journal*, Des Spence, M.D., a general practitioner from Glasgow argued that antidepressants are far too overprescribed. He cites the Cochrane review that found only about one in seven depressed patients benefit from antidepressant drugs.

The newer antidepressant drugs like Zoloft and Wellbutrin are SSRIs. This stands for "synaptic serotonin re-uptake inhibitors." They artificially raise levels of serotonin in the brain by preventing their normal re-uptake into neurons or nerve cells. This artificially floods the brain with serotonin. Some argue this extra serotonin helps improve symptoms of depression.

But is that really true?

Through my work in forensic medicine, I see case after case of chronically depressed patients. They were "successfully" treated with SSRIs. But then they promptly committed suicide. The treatment was a success, but the patient died.

Here's part of the problem...

SSRIs treat only a symptom of depression. They do nothing about the *underlying* causes.

When people are depressed, they turn inward. They close themselves off. And they lack energy to carry out actions. Instead, they just endlessly think thoughts, many of them negative. But they take no action.

Now give that person Prozac. You haven't changed anything about the *cause* of the depression. But suddenly they have energy. Including the energy to carry out their suicidal thoughts. And that they do.

So, how do you start down this troubled road?

It begins with the very definition of clinical depression.

Let's look at both the old and the controversial, new editions of the *Diagnostic and Statistical Manual of Mental Disorders*. Both editions define clinical depression as two weeks of "low mood."

It doesn't take a doctorate to see that this definition is far too loose. Indeed, this very flawed definition of the disease may be the root of the problem. It led to the widespread "medicalization" of what should be just normal chapters in human life!

Is it any surprise that antidepressant prescriptions increased by almost 10 percent in 2011? This represents the largest increase in prescription medicines across the board! And this number is on track to continue to grow in coming decades.

And, some parties are in a good mood indeed about the overuse of antidepressants. In fact, three-quarters of those who write the definitions of "low mood" used in the psychiatric manual have links to drug companies!

Mental illness may be the perfect condition for the drug industry. And drug makers couldn't be happier with the growing numbers diagnosed with depression.

"Low mood" may be incurable—not surprising, considering the treatment with SSRIs. It's common—not surprising, given the definition. It's long-term—but why, if the treatment is in fact any good? And it involves multiple medications. Yes—I'd say it's *the* perfect disease for the drug industry!

Modern psychiatry's relationship with the drug industry has created a therapeutic drug mindset to treat mental illness. Now psychiatrists can simply write a prescription, just like…"real doctors!"

Have we completely abandoned the more time-intensive approaches involving psychoanalysis, talk therapies, and even spiritual dimensions?

I hope not.

Sometimes a "low mood" is an accurate and appropriate response to reality. You cannot simply medicate it away.

Studies show that mildly depressed people can more accurately assess circumstances. Plus, they're more effective at dealing with them. And they're better at predicting real outcomes.

Perhaps our "low mood" is our body's natural response to perceiving "all is not well." Perhaps it is part of the body's "fight-or-flight" defense system. But we lack the energy to fight. So we "stand down… conserve…and withdraw." All the while, we stay "on alert."

Perhaps these drugs take away some human wisdom that we all need to feel sometimes.

Guidelines from the National Institute for Health and Clinical Excellence do not support the use of antidepressants for mild depression. Or necessarily for moderate depression. Instead, it favors psychological talk-based therapies. And for mild to moderate depression, the use of herbal remedies such as St. John's can be effective.

Now, I'm not saying that depression isn't a real problem. It *is* debilitating for many millions of Americans. But I don't recommend trying to artificially manipulate your serotonin levels as a treatment for any disease.

There are several treatments you can try to help your body heal naturally and restore its own proper levels of serotonin, acetylcholine and other neurochemicals.

Chapter 86

A natural depression treatment that works wonders

Seasonal Affective Disorder (SAD) is a type of depression that typically strikes during the winter, when days are shorter and there is less sunshine. Doctors often treat SAD with "light box" therapy. During light therapy sessions, you sit or work near a light box and the light enters your eyes indirectly.

Some researchers are finally "thinking outside the box" and have found light therapy also helps treat other types of depression not brought on by seasonal light deprivation.

In a recent study supported by the Canadian Institutes for Health Research, researchers randomly assigned 122 adults with major depression not related to SAD to one of four treatment groups.

The first group received 30 minutes of light treatment per day and a placebo pill. The second group used a "placebo" device that didn't provide actual light therapy and took Prozac. The third group used the placebo device and a placebo pill. And the fourth group received both actual light therapy and Prozac.

After eight weeks, researchers used a widely recognized depression scale to evaluate the participants' mental and emotional state.

Placebo outperforms antidepressant

First and foremost, Prozac showed no benefit over placebo.

No surprise there. Other studies consistently show the same thing (particularly when patients also receive a lot of attention from a health professional).

Among those who used a placebo device and took a placebo pill, about 30 percent of participants still showed improvement. Again, this finding demonstrates the benefits of a health professional paying any kind of attention to these patients.

By contrast, among those patients who used the placebo device and took Prozac, only 20 percent showed improvement.

So—the drug + placebo device performed worse than the placebo pill + placebo device. In other words, it appears the drug actually counteracted or negated any potential beneficial placebo effect!

And what about the group who got the real light therapy and the placebo pill? They fared even better yet—about 40 percent of them went into remission in just eight weeks.

Of course, the researchers still recommended giving Prozac together with light therapy because that combination saw a small bump in benefits. But antidepressants carry many harmful and dangerous side effects. In fact, a recent investigation shows that antidepressants cause 15 times as many suicides as the FDA reports.

From this study, I came away with two major impressions.

First, placebo continues to offer greater benefits than drugs for this major mental health condition. Secondly, light therapy performs even better than placebo alone.

Overall, patients tolerated the light treatment well. Researchers don't fully understand *why* it works. For seasonal affective disorder, it may help correct disturbances in the body's internal biological clock, or circadian rhythm. For non-SAD depression, it may work through the same "mechanism of action." But we just don't know at this point.

Isn't it enough — for now — to know it DOES work?

You can buy light boxes at drugstores and other retail outlets for less than $100. And some insurance even plans cover them. Treatment involves sitting in front of the light box for 30 minutes as soon as possible after waking. You can do it while eating breakfast or just working at your desk or on the computer.

Remember also that winter is the time of year when vitamin D levels decline, if you don't take regular vitamin D supplements. Research I reported from the U.K. a couple years ago demonstrated that those with low mood during winter had lower vitamin D levels, which explains a lot.

So make sure to take 10,000 IU daily of vitamin D. You can find it in liquid form, which may be easier to swallow with juice or water.

Chapter 87

Nature improves well-being in older adults

My daughter knows firsthand the power of spending time in Nature. She now works as a Maryland State Park Ranger. And under a wonderful governor, her state now funds a "Youth Park Ranger" program where urban children have an opportunity to get outside in Nature. I can't think of a simpler, healthier program for both mind and body.

My daughter's new Nature program is for children, but new research out of the University of Minnesota shows spending time in green and blue spaces (environments with running or still water) offers many health benefits to older people too.

As I often say, spending time in Nature every day improves your quality of life at any age. It measurably reduces stress. It also promotes physical, mental and spiritual healing. People can attain these health benefits by spending time outside to "get away from it all."

Fortunately, you don't have to embark on a Lewis & Clark expedition to gain the powerful benefits...

The new study shows exposure to small natural elements—such as a koi pond or a bench among flowers—benefitted older adults. In fact, these small green and blue spaces promoted feelings of renewal, restoration, and spiritual connection in adults ages 65 to 86.

They also provided places for social engagement and interaction, both planned and impromptu, with family and friends.

Researchers found access to blue and green spaces encouraged men and women to simply get out the door. It helped them maintain a structured daily schedule. Also, it helped offset the effects of chronic illness, disability and isolation. As a result, quality of life indicators showed decreases in boredom, isolation and loneliness. And improvements in their sense of accomplishment and purpose.

You can easily seek small connections to Nature. I always recommend spending time in and near water. I suppose it's only natural for me, since I spent a lot of time as a child on the coast of northern New England. And still do today, in New England and Florida.

Research shows movement in water is one of the best, healthiest, safest, and most restorative forms of physical activity. Also, simply spending time on the water or along the waterfront can help you relax and find a spiritual connection.

At the end of the fifth paragraph, in the very first chapter, of that great American novel *Moby Dick*, Herman Melville poetically writes, "Yes, as everyone knows, meditation and water are wedded forever."

I find many busy people think they don't have time or opportunities to connect with Nature or meditate on a daily basis.

But even in the middle of your busy life, you can find that "waterfront" for contemplation, spiritual connection and relaxation right in your own "mind's eye," anytime, every day.

You don't have to go away to a Buddhist Monastery, or even to the seashore, to get the benefits of practicing meditation.

Research shows practicing mindfulness as a young and middle-aged adult has many brain benefits. Imaging studies demonstrate that mindfulness meditation helps stave off dementia and can help you achieve healthy aging.

My advice for healthy aging is pretty simple:

1. Focus on overall wellbeing—mental and social health, as well as physical fitness.

2. Get out the door daily, even if it's just around the block or to the corner park.

3. Make contact with Nature an everyday priority. Sit in a park, listen to a water fountain, or sit among the plants in a garden.

Late summer and early fall is a special time of year, especially here along the New England coast. Here, the beaches are perfect for those contemplative and restorative walks along the water.

Chapter 88

Getting to the point of mood disorders

Today, modern psychiatrists like to talk about the semi-imaginary, chemical "imbalances" that cause mood disorders. They say they can correct the "imbalance" simply by adjusting the levels of certain chemicals in the brain, such as serotonin. Trouble is, they don't have any clue about the effects on all the <u>other</u> brain chemicals involved.

Plus, that approach assumes treating mood disorders is like doing an experiment with the Gibson chemistry set you used in middle school. Of course, according to all the latest research, this approach has been a disaster for mental health, public health, and even public safety.

The truth is—mental disorders are far more complex than most modern psychiatrists will admit.

Depressed men and women lived "normal lives" without drugs

In my view, we had a better understanding of the complexity of mental illness in the 19th century, when doctors considered the spiritual dimensions. And because they lacked modern drugs, doctors "prescribed" what they called "moral therapy" for patients with mental disorders such as depression.

Instead of locking away depressed patients—or numbing them with drugs—doctors allowed those struggling with mental disorders to live with others who were "normal." The mentally ill patients could then observe the ways other people reacted to and processed "reality." It helped the patients build a fund of positive experiences in their mental bank that they could draw from when they needed emotional reserves.

This approach isn't so different in principle from the 20th century's behavioral therapy and today's cognitive-behavioral therapies (CBI). Studies show these techniques are very effective, particularly in conjunction with other mind-body techniques like mindfulness meditation.

Spirit and consciousness are inherent to human existence…and certainly to our perception of it. But modern-day reductionists seem to think molecular models explain everything about our existence.

Fundamental physicists, who study the most basic aspects of reality itself, know better. They know life is far more complex than we currently comprehend.

In fact, astrophysicists made an observation that finally proved the final part of Einstein's General Theory of Relativity that he put forth a century ago. And many experts believe ancient Ayurveda and Chinese medicine probably understood some of these "cosmic" effects thousands of years before Einstein.

Chinese medicine offers deeper insights to depression

Practitioners of Chinese medicine have a deep understanding of the human existence as well. They too consider mood problems as spiritual problems. And they began using the acupuncture needle 2,000 years ago as a potent tool to tap into the essence or spirit, by bypassing the more material manifestations. In fact, an ancient description described acupuncture as the "spiritual pivot."

Now—let's go forward 2,000 years…

New research shows that acupuncture alleviates depression with insomnia. In Traditional Chinese Medicine, they call depression associated with insomnia "depressive insomnia." People with this condition have difficulty falling asleep. And they experience a disruption of sleep by dreams, generalized insomnia, and emotional volatility.

Western medical science is even beginning to understand the connection between these two disorders. In fact, in a recent study, researchers compared acupuncture to mirtazapine, an older antidepressant drug, in patients who suffer from depression with insomnia.

The researchers divided the participants into two groups. The first group received acupuncture. The second group received mirtazapine drug therapy. The drug caused drowsiness (not to be confused with healthful sleep), dizziness, and vision problems, as well weight gain associated with increased appetite and constipation. By comparison, acupuncture was effective in 90 percent of cases to improve duration and quality of sleep for patients with depression. And it caused no notable side effects.

The successful treatment protocol involved acupuncture sessions every other day. By comparison, the drug group took a pill daily.

Of course, some would argue taking daily pills is more "convenient." I suppose it is more convenient as long as you find going through the day in a drowsy stupor, with dizziness and visual disturbances to be convenient. And you can't mind gaining weight while struggling with increased appetite and constipation (enough to be depressed, right there).

In my view, anyone who still prescribes antidepressant drugs—when there are other safe and effective methods—simply misses the point.

PART 8

NATURAL ANSWERS FOR AN IRONCLAD IMMUNE SYSTEM

Chapter 89

Your immune system's most powerful ally

It seems every time I sit back down to my computer, another study pops up about the importance of vitamin D. It's no surprise really—Vitamin D appears to benefit virtually every part of your body. And it seems to help protect you against nearly every chronic disease. Now, three new studies even illustrate vitamin D's incredible effect on the immune system.

In the first study, researchers looked at vitamin D and its effect on colon cancer risk. They matched 318 people with colon cancer against a control group of 624 men and women without colon cancer. All the participants had given blood samples in the 1990s, before the appearance of any cancer.

The researchers measured the vitamin D levels in these samples and found the higher the participants' vitamin D blood levels at the outset, the less likely they were to develop colorectal tumors. Vitamin D, the authors suggest, interacts with the immune system to prevent the growth of this type of malignancy.

In a second study, researchers found that vitamin D prolongs survival time in people with metastasized colon cancer (cases in which the cancer has spread beyond the original site in the body).

For this study, researchers followed 1,430 people with metastatic colon cancer. The patients in the lowest fifth for vitamin D levels survived for an average of 25 months. By comparison, patients in the highest fifth for vitamin D levels survived for an average of 33 months. That's 33 percent longer. In addition, higher vitamin D delayed any progression of the cancer from 10 to 12 months.

These findings make perfect sense.

You see, malignant tumors contain other types of cells besides the actual cancer cells, including T-lymphocytes or T-cells. These immune cells influence how fast a tumor grows or spreads. They attack cancer cells, which they consider "foreign," and can limit tumor growth. And research has shown that vitamin D is necessary to activate these T-cells.

In yet another recent study, researchers linked low vitamin D with poorer recovery after major surgery. For this study, researchers at Massachusetts General Hospital and Harvard Medical School measured vitamin D levels of patients admitted to the hospital's surgical intensive care unit (ICU). They found that ICU patients with low vitamin D blood levels spent more time on artificial respiratory support. Evidence links mechanical ventilation itself with a number of negative health outcomes. So getting off those breathing machines is a critical goal in critical care—and vitamin D helps.

Of course, we already knew that low vitamin D aggravates asthma and Chronic Obstructive Pulmonary Disease (COPD). Conversely, we know that boosting vitamin D levels improves lung function.

So a lot may come back to vitamin D's role in supporting immune system function. It appears this critical nutrient inhibits inflammation in the lungs, while boosting the immune system to defend against respiratory bacteria and viruses. Indeed, a balanced immune system *decreases* unhealthy inflammation, while *increasing* healthy immune response against microbes.

No simple-minded, single-function drug can do anything like that. All they do is put the system out of balance. They either boost the immune system artificially, which increases inflammation. Or they deaden it, which reduces inflammation, but leaves you vulnerable to infection (as with steroids).

It's remarkable that vitamin D positively influences the body's reaction to so many diseases—from cancer to lung diseases. And that something as simple as keeping up your vitamin D levels (as with daily supplementation) can translate into measurable and meaningful benefits—well beyond the high-cost, high-tech, and invasive modern medicine that we throw at these devastating diseases.

Unfortunately, the government-industrial-medical guidelines for vitamin D are so pathetically constrained by their focus only on bone health, just following the RDA for vitamin D simply won't provide the benefits this nutrient is capable of conferring.

You really need to take 5,000 IU of vitamin D daily. Even better, combine it with the natural powerhouse astaxanthin. You can now take them together as an easy-to-use and easy-to-absorb liquid.

P.S. A quick reminder: If you come down with the flu, you can safely take up to 20,000 IU of vitamin D per day just for the duration of the illness. This course will help your immune system fight the infection more effectively. And it will undoubtedly be a whole lot more effective than relying on the pathetic flu vaccine or Tamiflu drug treatment.

Chapter 90

The simple, natural ingredient on your fruits and vegetables that can protect you from foodborne illness

You've probably been warned not to judge a book by its cover...and that beauty is only skin deep. But when it comes to food safety, it's all on the surface.

In an attempt to better understand what contributes to food contamination, researchers recently conducted an experiment on two dozen varieties of common salad greens and tomatoes.

What they found challenged the conventional wisdom that rougher surfaces (like a kale leaf) would hide viruses and bacteria and make them harder to wash away.

Instead, the researchers discovered that vegetables that have a waxy layer—which naturally protects the plant against diseases and dehydration—had fewer viruses on their surface after washing, compared to their non-waxy counterparts.

The cleanest greens you can eat

Specifically, the researchers found a *thousand-times fewer* viral particles left on vegetables with a wax layer after being washed, compared to vegetables without this type of layer.

The waxiest produce (and therefore least likely to harbor viruses) included:

- Collard greens (Top Bunch variety)
- Kale (Starbor and Red Russian
- Cabbage (Alcosa and Gonzales)
- Tomatoes (Indigo Rose, Rose, and Sungold)
- Romaine lettuce (Outredgeous)

Other lettuces, endive, spinach, radicchio, arugula, and mustard greens had the lowest amounts of wax.

The science behind food safety

So why did the researchers focus on produce used in salads? Well, fruits and vegetables are exposed to viruses and other microbial contaminants in a number of ways. Among the top offenders are contaminated irrigation water, animal waste on the plants, and handling by farm workers.

When produce is cooked, it typically kills microbial contaminants. But when it's eaten raw, like in a salad, food safety can be particularly problematic.

To conduct the experiment, the researchers swabbed 24 varieties of raw salad greens and tomatoes with a swine virus that mimics human rotavirus—a common pathogen responsible for gastrointestinal infections. (There is a vaccine for rotavirus, but safety and ethical questions have made it the subject of great controversy).

The researchers washed the contaminated greens and tomatoes twice in a standard salt solution.

Then, they evaluated the surfaces of the vegetables at different levels of magnification. Not only were they looking for viruses, but also the amount and composition of waxes on the produce.

While viruses typically adhere to waxes at the molecular level, the researchers found that when a wax completely covers the surface of a fruit or vegetable, it repels water and makes it harder for viruses to stick.

While the researchers did their best to make this sound chemically complicated (and relevant), it's basically the same reason it's simpler to keep floors clean when they are waxed. As we all know, waxed surfaces are easier to wash—whether they're floors or fruits.

Hidden sources of wax on your produce

While wax may help cut contamination on produce, it's important to note that not all wax on fruits and vegetables is natural.

Conventionally and even organically grown produce may be artificially waxed to prevent moisture loss and dehydration, protect it from bruising during shipping, and increase its shelf life.

That's why you'll often see wax on apples, cucumbers, eggplant, citrus fruits, peppers, and potatoes.

Some of this added wax is from natural sources like carnauba (from the carnauba palm tree), beeswax, and shellac (from the lac beetle). But some of it is petroleum-based.

To ensure you're not eating petroleum, buy organic fruits and vegetables, which, by law, can only use natural waxes. Or you can buy directly from the grower—just visit your local farmer's market or sign up for community-supported (CSA) deliveries.

Unfortunately, the only way to remove any type of added wax is to peel the fruit or vegetable. And that can remove the nutrients that lie right below the skin.

While you should carefully wash all produce before eating, your salad may be that much safer (and nutritious) if you load it up with kale, cabbage, collards, tomatoes, and red romaine.

Watch out for pesticides too

Of course, there are other contaminants on produce besides microbes that can cause health issues. Particularly pesticides.

According to the nonprofit Environmental Working Group, nearly three-quarters of conventional produce samples tested by the USDA in 2014 contained pesticide residues. And the really disturbing thing is that the pesticides remained on fruits and vegetables even after they were washed. And in some cases, even after they were peeled!

Every year, the EWG releases its "Dirty Dozen"—the 12 types of conventional fruits and vegetables that are most contaminated with pesticides.

The 2016 Dirty Dozen includes strawberries, apples, nectarines, peaches, celery, grapes, cherries, spinach, tomatoes, sweet bell peppers, cherry tomatoes, and cucumbers.

And the EWG notes that hot peppers, kale, and collard greens can be contaminated with insecticides and pesticides that are particularly toxic.

So how can you avoid these deadly chemicals? It's simple. Just eat organic produce—which, by law, can't be sprayed with pesticides, insecticides, or chemical fertilizers.

Chapter 91

"Wonder vitamin" reduces lung disease flare-ups by 40 percent

You've probably been subjected to those ridiculous commercials featuring an elephant sitting on top of breathless lung disease sufferers. Aside from the question of whether any animals (or humans) were harmed in the making of these commercials, do you want to know the real elephant in the room?

New drugs like the one featured in this ad really have little to offer (other than the long list of side effects rattled off at the end of those annoying commercials). But the benefits of vitamins are hiding in plain sight.

In fact, a new British study showed that simple vitamin D supplements reduced flare-ups of chronic obstructive pulmonary disease (COPD) by over *40 percent.*

COPD includes lung conditions like emphysema and chronic bronchitis, and affects more than 12 million people in the U.S. So it's no wonder drug companies have gravitated toward this disease like a herd of stampeding elephants.

But, once again, the real results—and relief for patients suffering from COPD—are coming from nature, not big pharma.

Less inflammation, easier breathing

The study included 240 people with COPD. Half were given vitamin D supplements, and the other half received a placebo.

The researchers found that everyone in the vitamin D group had less severe and shorter COPD flare-ups. And among people who started the study with low vitamin D levels, the results were even more dramatic.

Of course, people in darker, colder climates like the U.K. (and much of the U.S.) are generally deficient in vitamin D. In the study, 87 percent of participants had inadequate vitamin D status. The people who had D blood levels lower than 50 nmol/L had the most pronounced reduction in COPD flare-ups.

As you know, vitamin D has many effects in the body. In this case, the researchers believe it suppressed the inflammatory cells that trigger lung disease flare-ups.

How much is enough?

For optimum health, I recommend 5,000 IU of vitamin D3 daily to ensure there's a constant, adequate amount of the vitamin in the body at all times.

This dose is substantially more than the woefully inadequate 600 IU per day the government recommends for people under age 70 (if you're over age 70, you get a "whopping" 800 IU a day). But these outdated recommendations are based on old, inadequate vitamin D research and fearmongering about "excess" vitamin D.

Doctors often worry that fat-soluble vitamins, like D, can be dangerous because they are stored in the body. But lets look at it the other way around. In the COPD study, participants were given the equivalent of about 120,000 IU of vitamin D *all at once*, and then got another dose of the same size two months later.

Our ability to store high doses of vitamin D actually shows how much this vitamin is needed in the body at all times. Furthermore, it proves that large quantities can be and *are* safely stored in the body.

So a supposed "megadose" of vitamin D is simply safely stored away for later use. What's so dangerous about that, doc?

It's certainly far safer than the anti-inflammatory steroid drugs that many doctors prescribe for COPD. Steroids disrupt the body's metabolism and immune system about as much as vitamin D supports them.

But unfortunately, few people manage to leave a doctor's office without a drug prescription. And these days, vitamins are primarily used and tested in *addition to*, not *instead of,* drugs.

Imagine how healthy our lungs—and our entire bodies—might be in a properly nourished, drug-free world.

Chapter 92

Treat your cold or flu with echinacea and elderberry—not Tamiflu

As soon as you find yourself coming down with a cold or flu, there are effective, scientifically proven natural approaches you can take.

For decades, there has been growing research on the ability of the herb echinacea (the Native American purple cornflower) to prevent or limit the severity and duration of colds or flu.

And now, new research shows that echinacea combined with extract from elderberries is *just as effective* as the expensive and dangerous drug Tamiflu for reducing or ending flu symptoms.

Plus, people who take Tamiflu are over <u>twice</u> as likely to have their flu turn into pneumonia, bronchitis, or sinusitis than those who take echinacea and elderberry.

I wish I had known this when I was a young adult in medical training at the University of Pennsylvania—home to the nation's oldest hospital and medical school. There was not much that could keep me and my colleagues down. But we all dreaded getting the "chop rot" from the Children's Hospital of Philadelphia (CHoP). Mysterious viruses would emerge from children cooped up in this hospital. And they could "chop" down a healthy young adult in the prime of life—at least for a few days.

Fortunately for those kids and my colleagues, Tamiflu wasn't around then. As I have written in the past, this drug has serious side effects. Not only nausea, vomiting, and headaches—which are bad enough—but also kidney disorders and psychiatric syndromes.

But thanks to this new research, we now know an echinacea/elderberry combo is just as effective as Tamiflu, with none of the worrisome side effects.

How the flu flew away

Researchers in the Czech Republic recruited 473 people who previously had influenza symptoms for less than 48 hours. Each study participant was given either Tamiflu or a hot drink containing an echinacea extract supplemented with elderberry.

After one day, 2 percent of the echinacea group and 4 percent of the Tamiflu group had mild or no flu symptoms. After five days, 50 percent of the echinacea group and 49 percent of the Tamiflu group were symptom free. And after 10 days, 90 percent of the echinacea group and 85 percent of the Tamiflu group had recovered.

Echinacea and elderberry was particularly impressive when it came to preventing more serious health issues. Seven percent of the Tamiflu group ended up getting pneumonia, bronchitis, sinusitis, or gastrointestinal issues like nausea or vomiting. But only 3 percent of the echinacea group had these respiratory problems, and none of them suffered from the gastrointestinal issues.

While this study used a proprietary echinacea and elderberry blend from Europe, other studies indicate that a daily dose of echinacea tea spiked with elderberry extract is effective and makes a pleasant hot beverage. I don't think there is sufficient evidence to recommend doses. Like many herbal infusions, just brew a concoction that tastes good and drink it often. The key is to start this process within 48 hours after your first cold or flu symptoms.

And remember not to take echinacea unless you are coming down with a cold or flu. Otherwise, you run the risk of chronically overstimulating your immune system. Which, ironically, could increase your susceptibility to colds and flu.

Other ways to fight colds and flu

Of course, most basically healthy people eventually recover from colds and flu without any treatment. But why be miserable any longer than you have to?

Bolster your immune system throughout the year, and you'll make yourself much less susceptible to the viruses your family brings home from school or work.

A good approach is to take a good-quality B complex every day, along with 500 mg of vitamin C twice per day. And don't forget daily doses of 10,000 IU of vitamin D, 400 mg of vitamin E, 200 mcg of selenium, and 35 mg of zinc—which you want to be taking anyway for their many brain and body benefits.

There is a lot of talk about high-dose vitamin C, but your body can only effectively make use of 500 mg at a time.

You can, however, really stock up on vitamin D. Some of my natural physician colleagues say from their personal and clinical experience, it's best to take 20,000 IU of D per day when you feel you are coming down with a cold or flu. I'm not aware of any studies on that higher dose, however.

Finally, if you're reading this on a touch screen, make sure you frequently wash your hands or use alcohol-based hand sanitizers. That's a good idea in any circumstance, but particularly for touch screens, which are a great invention—for viruses and other diseases that are passed along by touching.

Chapter 93

The hidden, ugly truth about vaccines

Since the start of the measles outbreak in California, we've heard plenty about vaccines from the usual "experts" in the media and the talking heads in the academic-industrial-government medical complex. The U.S. Surgeon General finally weighed in on the topic with nothing more than a deafening echo of what the lame stream media reports were already spouting.

Of course, vaccination is a complex issue. And we could really use a non-politicized Surgeon General who's actually an expert on infectious diseases to guide us through these complex times. For example, when I worked with former Surgeon General C. Everett Koop during the Reagan administration, he always led the charge on important public health issues. But the Obama administration chose the current Surgeon General because he's an expert on gun control and partisan, political fundraising.

Politics aside, it's very distressing that we never hear about so many of the scientific facts concerning vaccines. Perhaps they think we can't handle the truth. Because the truth is not pretty.

You see, the measles outbreak in California involved many vaccinated people who nonetheless contracted the disease. Similarly, there was an outbreak of mumps among healthy, young professional hockey players, many of whom had been vaccinated.

You may wonder why and how all these people contract these infectious diseases when they've already been vaccinated.

The truth is, getting vaccinated doesn't guarantee you won't get the disease.

In fact, in an interview, Gabe Mirkin, M.D., explained the situation perfectly. He said, "It's not that vaccines don't work at all, it's that we were led to believe they offer lifelong immunity when they don't. How on Earth do 20-year-old men on the Pittsburgh Penguins hockey team all come down with mumps if they were vaccinated as kids?"

Gabe is actually an old friend and colleague from back in the days when we lived in Maryland. Now, he lives here in Florida like me. During the 1990s, he was one of two regular physicians in the D.C. area (the other was Michael Emmer, M.D.) who I ever visited as a patient. And I recommended them both to my family and friends. Gabe actually practiced science-based medicine, instead of just handing out pills as prescribed by big pharma.

And Gabe nailed the hidden, ugly truth about vaccines: They aren't guarantees.

In fact, the only way to **guarantee** you'll get full immunity is to get the disease itself. This also confers natural immunity to members of the population.

When I was a child, everyone came down with chicken pox, German measles, measles, and mumps. Mostly, we were sick for a few days from school and that was all. Then we had lifelong immunity.

Anyone who missed getting these largely self-limiting infections naturally as a child ran the risk of coming down with them as an adult— when the infections could be far more dangerous. Nobody worried about exposing children in school because parents **wanted** their children to get, and get over, these common infections quickly while they were young.

In addition, when children are breastfed, they continue to receive "passive immunity" from the mother during the most vulnerable period of infancy. Then, well-nourished and healthy children who spend time outdoors generally develop stronger immune systems that can withstand the common childhood infections.

On the other side of the coin, some vaccines can and **do** have deadly and debilitating consequences. For example, the HPV vaccine—given to innocent young girls and boys—is a national scandal. In some cases, patients develop devastating neurological diseases as a direct consequence of vaccination.

Unlike our gun control expert Surgeon General, Senator Rand Paul, a physician, is one of the few "talking heads" in Washington, D.C., actually qualified to give a medical opinion. As he quickly pointed out, no one seems to talk about the millions of reports citing the negative consequences of vaccines. We only hear the parroting of the party line about the "indisputable" evidence supporting vaccines.

But even well-established vaccines have their problems. In fact, there is a pending lawsuit against the MMR (mumps, measles, rubella) vaccine, which states the U.S. government purchased an estimated four million doses of mislabeled and misbranded vaccine for over a decade or more.

Plus, vaccines contain many dangerous ingredients. According to the Centers for Disease Control (CDC) itself, common additives include: aluminum, antibiotics, albumin, formaldehyde, monosodium glutamate (MSG), and thimerosal (containing mercury).

Many people have deadly allergic reactions to antibiotics, albumin or MSG. Mercury is toxic to brain and nervous tissue. Experts suspect aluminum has the same side effects. And, of course, formaldehyde is a metabolic poison used to embalm dead tissue.

Amazingly, the Environmental Protection Agency, California, and other states have banned dumping several of these chemicals into the environment. Yet the CDC encourages doctors to dump them into the bodies of our children!

So—what's the result of all this vaccination in our children?

American children are the most highly vaccinated people on the planet. These poor little pin cushions receive some 49 doses of 14 different vaccines before the age of six. But they're also among the most chronically ill children in Western nations.

A final note that nobody else seems to be catching on to…

Doctors often give Tylenol (acetaminophen) before, during, and/or after administering a vaccine. This practice conveniently but inappropriately prevents the presence of a fever from stopping administration of a "scheduled" vaccine. But a child with a fever should never receive a vaccine because it's a sign the immune system is already over-stimulated.

Furthermore, Tylenol is a metabolic poison. In fact, one researcher recently uncovered a link between children who received Tylenol at the time of vaccination and the development of autism.

The vaccine industry is a risk-free proposition for big pharma. In fact, federal law prevents anyone from suing the manufacturer of a vaccine for the harm it does. Nor is it a risk for the academic-government-industrial medical complex. The public bears *all* the risk. And there's no recourse for the citizens who ultimately pay for it all.

Chapter 94

Which vaccines do you really need?

I've talk about the pressure we're all under to get an annual flu vaccine. But you and I both know your healthcare providers aren't likely to be content with just one vaccination. They want to inoculate you against a whole host of health conditions.

Pneumonia. Shingles. Tetanus. Even childhood diseases like mumps and measles.

But do you really need all—or *any*—of these vaccines?

Confusing immunization "facts" can spread as quickly as…a virus. So it's no wonder you may be concerned about vaccinations. Especially as you age, and are bombarded with propaganda about more "essential" vaccines you "must" have.

At the same time, there are increasing concerns that the more vaccines you get, the more imbalanced your immune system becomes. And an imbalanced immune system can make you more susceptible to chronic diseases. Not to mention the public health consequences of eliminating natural immunity in the population.

Then there's the shocking lack of science (*and* lack of effectiveness) of the government's influenza vaccine. It's certainly enough to make you wonder whether it's worth getting jabbed with *any* vaccination needle.

Based on my concerns about the flu vaccine, you may think I'm against vaccines in general.

But let me be clear. I am not anti-vaccine. I am pro-science.

Throughout my career, I have witnessed important developments in the history and science of vaccines. And I've found that some of the more recent vaccines are ones we would actually be better off *not* getting.

So let's take a look at the science behind common vaccines. And whether that science suggests you should—or <u>shouldn't</u>—get a particular vaccine.

But first, it's helpful to know the dramatic history of vaccines. And how that has led to where we are today. An environment where healthcare workers feel increasing pressure to inoculate everybody for everything.

Immunization goes back over 200 years

Some of the greatest advancements in modern medicine resulted from the ability to vaccinate people against deadly infections.

For instance, Dr. Edward Jenner's experiments with cowpox in England led to average village doctors throughout the Western world being able to provide smallpox immunity to their patients by the late 1700s. Centuries before, Eastern doctors accomplished the same thing for some residents of the vast Chinese empire.

Of course, neither East nor West knew then about viruses or the germ theory of disease. They just based their findings on trial and error and observation.

When the germ theory did become widely understood and accepted, it led to the development of more vaccines during the late 19th and early 20th centuries. Some were developed by doctors who worked in the same job I held myself, almost 100 years later, at Walter Reed Army Medical Center (including Dr. Walter Reed himself.)

One of the most notable vaccines to emerge in the mid-20th century was the injectable polio vaccine, created by Dr. Jonas Salk, whom I once had the privilege of meeting later in his career.

The debate over polio vaccines

Interestingly, Salk's vaccine kills the polio virus once it enters the bloodstream from the gastrointestinal tract. This is important because if polio gets into the bloodstream, it can then migrate into the central nervous system (CNS)—causing the dreaded "infantile paralysis." But the vast majority of younger children who are exposed to the polio virus just end up with a GI infection. The virus never gets into the CNS. And children who get this GI polio infection develop lifelong immunity to the disease—without being vaccinated.

Dr. Albert Sabin later developed the oral polio vaccine. But there is a problem with the oral polio vaccine—it prevents natural GI infections caused by the virus, which means that children can't develop the natural immunity I mentioned above.

Without natural immunity, doctors have to make sure to vaccinate each and every child. Otherwise, there would be pockets where there was no immunity at all—and every child would be susceptible to polio when it periodically came through the population. And potentially at older ages, when contracting the virus is more likely to cause paralysis (as in the case of Franklin D. Roosevelt, who got polio as a young adult).

Scientific debate between oral and injectable polio vaccines continues to this day. I had my own "debatable" encounter with polio when I was doing fieldwork in Southeast Asia in 1977.

There was an outbreak of polio in a jungle village, and the local government health officials refused to investigate it. Fortunately, Catholic priests from the nearby Columbian Mission were happy to guide me and help map the outbreak—which we traced to a contaminated common water source.

I turned in the maps and data to the local health authorities, who refused to do anything. Instead, they castigated me as a foreigner for interfering and "insulting" what must have been their very fragile egos. They even lodged incendiary complaints against me with my sponsoring organization back in the U.S. It was a shocking and dispiriting introduction to government public health for me.

The eradication of smallpox

Like the polio vaccine, smallpox vaccination was another great global achievement. It was so successful that during the late 1970s, medical teams working for the World Health Organization were able to isolate the last remaining pockets of smallpox in the horn of Africa.

As a new medical anthropologist, I was asked by a senior health professional at the CDC (which was good at doing its job back then because it still focused on its mission against infectious diseases) to speak at an annual American Anthropological Association meeting in the 1980s. You see, these infectious disease doctors realized they needed anthropologists to figure out the cultural and social factors that were keeping people from getting vaccinated. So the CDC wanted me to help generate awareness about completing the eradication of smallpox and other infections.

Unfortunately, I learned the ivory-tower anthropologists were not really interested in anything as relevant as helping to eradicate an infectious disease that had been a scourge of human populations since earliest recorded history. Although many did make politically correct careers writing about how smallpox and other diseases introduced by Europeans had decimated Native American and other populations hundreds of years ago.

But in terms of contemporary medical practice, these academic anthropologists were more interested in studying how indigenous concepts of belly buttons related to beliefs about causes of illness (or maybe it was their own belly buttons they were interested in studying—I never quite got that straight).

Thankfully, my faculty advisor for my MD/PhD in anthropology, Nobel laureate Baruch Blumberg, wasn't one of those ivory-tower investigators. He did early research with Dr. Irving Millman to develop a hepatitis B vaccine before Merck took over the research. (Blumberg was awarded the Nobel Prize in 1976 for discovery of the virus.)

How the "golden age" is turning into a bureaucratic rage

The idea of being inoculated against every conceivable virus may sound appealing in terms of disease prevention. But as with pharmaceutical drugs, it seems the last generation of vaccines has really stuck us with some problems.

Part of this is due to the emergence of a sub-specialized field of "virology" that includes many scientists and physicians. These careerists see every health issue as a nail that needs to be pounded. So they focus on developing the technology to "hammer" viruses with vaccines.

Take the human papillomavirus (HPV) vaccine, for instance. This vaccine is very controversial, as I have often reported. In fact, some doctors and whistleblowers have described it as the greatest medical scandal of the century.

Why? First of all, in terms of the actual infection, HPV is not any more dangerous than viruses that cause the common cold. And there is no data showing the vaccine actually prevents cervical cancer. Finally, the vaccine works against only a few of the HPV strains—and the latest concern is that vaccinated women may be more likely to get infected with higher-risk strains of the virus.

Plus, there are already excellent, safe screening techniques that effectively help prevent cervical cancer (which is already relatively rare and becoming more rare) without any vaccination.

Sadly, the push to give every girl the HPV vaccine is less about public health and more about profits. Which is ironic because previous generations of vaccine developers, including Dr. Jonas Salk, gave away their creations for the benefit of humankind.

But that all changed when today's big pharma entered the vaccine industry. Drug companies started complaining they couldn't make enough money from vaccines. So our "public servants" in Congress got into the act of vaccination.

These bureaucrats were convinced to pass legislation making drug companies "immune" from malpractice lawsuits for all of the harm done by their vaccines. Instead, there is a vaccine injury compensation fund (which the taxpayers are stuck with). But according to many consumers, trying to get compensation for vaccine injuries is like trying to pass the proverbial camel through the eye of a needle.

So where are we today? Certainly, there are too many useless and dangerous vaccines. But that doesn't mean all of the current vaccines are worthless.

Vaccines you should consider

Pneumonia. Dr. Robert Austrian, my former professor at the University of Pennsylvania and colleague at the College of Physicians of Philadelphia, spent his career developing an effective vaccine for pneumonia.

Pneumonia is the eighth leading cause of death in Americans. And people over age 65 are particularly at risk. The good news is that the vaccine prevents pneumonia in 60 to 80 percent of people over age 65. That's why I think older people—and younger people with chronic diseases or immunological problems—may want to consider getting this vaccine. One vaccination will usually last your entire lifetime.

Chickenpox/shingles. Painful (and now distastefully well-publicized) shingles outbreaks are triggered by the same virus that causes chickenpox during childhood. If you had chickenpox or were vaccinated against it, the virus may be reactivated in later life as shingles.

One clinical trial of 38,000 people age 60 or older found that the shingles vaccine reduced the chance of suffering an outbreak by 51 percent. You've got better odds if you're under age 70—the vaccine was effective for 64 percent of that age group. But for those age 70 or older, the vaccine only reduced the risk of shingles by 34 percent.

So consider those odds when deciding whether to have a shingles vaccine.

Another factor to take into account is that shingles appears to have become much more common since universal childhood vaccination for chickenpox started. So that suggests you may have more protection from shingles if you actually had chickenpox as a child—rather than receiving the vaccine.

If you've never had chickenpox or been vaccinated against it, I recommend getting the vaccine. It can be very dangerous to get chickenpox as an adult. You may end up with serious complications like encephalitis, myocarditis (inflammation of the heart), or pancreatitis.

Vaccines that probably aren't worth it

Measles, mumps, rubella (MMR). Healthcare workers may try to tell you that even if you had this trifecta of diseases as a child, you still need a vaccination as an adult. But there is no reason for older adults to get this vaccine.

Even the vaccine-pushing CDC admits that if you were born before 1957, you're "generally considered immune" to measles and mumps.[3] You don't need any so-called "booster shot."

But today's children must have the MMR vaccine to be allowed to go to school (and of course, children have to go to school—typically without choice of public schools). So that means natural measles, mumps, and rubella immunity will soon be gone from the general population, requiring all children in every new generation to get the vaccine. Forever. What a gold mine in those steel needles.

Meningitis. The only time this vaccine is really useful is for young people who live in close quarters like college dorms, boarding schools, and camps where the disease has been known to spread. It seems that today the typical college student is more interested in having multiple "close contacts" than, say, hitting the books, so it might make sense for them.

But for older adults, the risk of getting meningitis is very low, making the vaccine unnecessary.

Tetanus. This vaccine doesn't protect against a virus, but rather against a toxic chemical made by anaerobic bacteria that hide deep in the soil. This bacteria can burrow deep into your injured tissues and cause infection.

Many doctors say they have never seen a single case of tetanus (lockjaw) in their entire medical careers. And the vaccine requires a booster every 10 years—which may unbalance the immune system. Taking all of that into account, tetanus vaccines may simply not be worth it—at any age.

Don't succumb to the politics of vaccinations

The big questions when it comes to all vaccines are really a matter of elementary logic. If vaccines work so well and provide immunity to those who get them, why are so many parents, teachers, physicians, and government bureaucrats so insistent about taking away all choice and forcing *everyone* to get potentially dangerous vaccines—because somehow the unvaccinated are a threat to others?

If you get a vaccine and become immune, then you are protected from that infection. Regardless of whether someone, or anyone, else is vaccinated and protected. So why bully, hector, and strong-arm everyone around you to get a vaccine for your own protection?

This issue came up in a recent Republican presidential debate. Three of the candidates, including two who are licensed physicians, raised serious questions about mandatory vaccination.

No matter where you come down on the subject, one thing is true. Without universal vaccination, there is still the opportunity for natural immunity to develop in the population (as it can with polio). But universal vaccination requires that everyone—everywhere, forever—get vaccines.

Bottom line: eliminating all natural immunity in the population may have long-term, unforeseen consequences for the human immune system and health.

So be aware and be informed the next time you hear you "must have" a certain vaccine. I always say the least medicine that works is the best medicine. Likewise, the fewer vaccines needed to sensibly protect your health, the better.

Chapter 95

7 natural ways to stay cold and flu free—
without vaccines

As you know, I and many others are troubled by the flu vaccine side effects that are reported in other countries (but that only some people, including my readers, ever seem to hear about in the U.S.). Serious side effects like convulsions, narcolepsy, and compromised immune systems.

And then there's the lack of evidence that this vaccine really works.

There is no evidence it really helps older people. There is no evidence it works in children. And last year's vaccine did not appear to work at all in anybody, anywhere.

So here's what I recommend. Every time a doctor, nurse, or pharmacist asks you to get a vaccine, ask them how much research they have done on the safety and effectiveness of the vaccine.

I estimate that I perform about 20 hours of research per month on the latest findings worldwide on vaccines, including the flu vaccine. That's 240 hours per year. Does your doctor, nurse, or pharmacist do that much research on what he or she recommends?

If you really want to stump your healthcare providers, ask them why they're pushing flu vaccines when there are 7 simple steps everyone can do to protect themselves from cold and flu viruses *better* than a flu vaccine can.

And then hand them the following list.

My top cold and flu fighters

1.) Don't automatically shake hands. Did you know that Donald Trump may be the first politician not to shake hands? This is because "The Donald" practices germ avoidance. Maybe it is because the one thing he cannot afford is to be sick. After all, cold and flu viruses are spread by contact, and who knows where someone's hands have been?

2.) Regularly wipe down your keypads and phones. Hilary Clinton is another politician who is good at "wiping" things clean (or maybe not so good, according to the FBI)—like personal computer servers that hold government classified documents. But I digress. Wiping down surfaces can be a very healthy practice.

Phones and keypads can be germ-breeding grounds. And they come into close contact with mouths, eyes, ears, and hands—all of which are disease transfer and entry points. So wipe down these devices regularly with alcohol, an alcohol-based hand sanitizer, or slightly soapy water (do not soak!) regularly.

3.) Stay sanitary in public restrooms. You already know to wash your hands after using the bathroom. But public restroom sanitation goes beyond that. As I reported in the past, public restroom door handles, toilets, faucets, soap dispensers, and hand driers are all loaded with bacteria and viruses.

After you wash your hands with soap and water, avoid the hand dryer. Research shows it just blows bacteria and viruses throughout the restroom. Instead, dry your hands with a paper towel and then use that towel to open the door when you exit the bathroom. Doorknobs are *teeming* with bacteria and viruses—especially in public restrooms.

In your own bathroom, close the lid before you flush to cut down on airborne germs.

4.) Carry hand sanitizer in your car. Now that we have to pump our own gasoline (except on the New Jersey Turnpike), gas pumps have become some of the most contaminated surfaces anywhere.

Visit the restroom and wash up after pumping gas, or clean your hands with sanitizer. In fact, you should always keep alcohol-based hand sanitizer (that doesn't contain the toxic chemical triclosan) in your car. Spritz your steering wheel and stick shift (or run your hands over them while they're still wet after applying gel sanitizer) whenever you get in the car—especially after pumping gas.

5.) Give your purse, briefcase, or bag a boost. Think of how many germs your satchels literally sit on when you put them on the floor in public places. And then how those germs can transfer to your hands when you pick up your bag.

Hang the strap or handle of your briefcase or purse over the back of a chair or other hook, or simply put your bag on a chair or bench—not on the dirty floor.

6.) Hold your breath. If someone in a public place is sneezing or coughing, just turn away and hold your breath for a few seconds. This will help keep you from inhaling the germs released into the air. Then, avoid touching surfaces—and don't touch your face—until you can get to a less contaminated area.

This precaution reminds me of school sports physicals. To check for a hernia, the doctor says, "Turn your head and cough." The cough increases the pressure inside the abdomen, which can cause any hernia to appear. I used to wonder about the complex pressure dynamics involved in coughing while turning the head. When I got to medical school and asked about it, the professor laughed and said the school doctor was just avoiding getting repeatedly coughed in his face.

7.) Don't ever underestimate the importance of sleep. There's plenty of evidence showing that lack of sleep increases your risk of getting a cold, flu, or other illness.

And now a new study quantifies that risk. Researchers found that people who sleep less than six hours a night are over *four times* more likely to get a cold than those who get more shuteye. (The study was done in Pittsburgh rather than New York because, you know…it's the "city that never sleeps.")

The researchers sequestered 164 volunteers in a hotel. Each study participant was given a cold virus via nasal drops, and then monitored for a week. The researchers discovered that the people who slept fewer than six hours per night were 4.2 times more likely to come down with a cold compared to people who slept seven or more hours per night. And people who spent less than five hours sleeping were 4.5 times more likely to get a cold.

In other words, just one extra hour in bed each night can help you avoid having to spend days in bed with a severe cold.

In fact, lack of sleep was the biggest risk factor for coming down with a cold in this study—more than age, stress levels, alcohol intake, ethnicity, education, or income. Even the great villain of government public health, smoking, was less likely to cause a cold than lack of sleep.

So if you're wondering why it seems so many people these days always seem to have a cold, it may simply be because of lack of sleep. Something the CDC has identified as yet another public health "epidemic."

Along with illnesses, the CDC says insufficient sleep is linked to motor vehicle accidents, industrial disasters, and medical errors. (When I was in medical training, we were told that young physicians don't need sleep, but apparently, sleep-deprived doctors finally "woke up" to the fact that doctors are human too).

The National Sleep Foundation did a survey in 2013 that found one out of five Americans get less than six hours of sleep on work nights, and more than half get less than seven hours' sleep. The U.S. ranked lowest in total sleep hours among the six countries surveyed.

Another new study sheds light on how the relationship between sleep and immunity works.

It has to do with how your body has a built-in 24-hour "clock" that regulates hormonal functions, physiology, and behavior. This clock is called the circadian cycle. And this cycle is found in every animal and plant that has a lifespan longer than 24 hours, including single-celled organisms. It's another factor that shows how closely we are tied to nature, or should be.

The researchers who conducted this study noted that disruption of the circadian cycle affects almost everyone in modern society, due to factors like artificial lighting, working at night and shift work, jet lag, and even the light emitted at night by cell phones and tablets.

In the study, the researchers disrupted the normal 24-hour clock of mice by putting them on 20-hour clock out of synch with the day-and-night, light-and-dark cycle.

The researchers found that even though the mice still got enough sleep, their immune response wasn't normal. Which made them more vulnerable to illness. That suggests that for good health and immunity, not just the *amount* of sleep but the *quality* and *timing* of that sleep are important.

In other words, if you want to fight flu, colds, and other viruses, get enough sleep *and* go to bed and wake up around the same time each day. (This gives new meaning to the old Italian-American saying about "going to the mattresses.")

And of course, help keep your immune system strong with a healthy diet and a supplement regimen that includes a high-quality B vitamin complex every day, 250 mg of vitamin C twice a day, and 10,000 IU of vitamin D per day.

Chapter 96

A cure for the common cold (hiding in plain sight)

My late father-in-law, Jack O'Leary, used to ask me long ago why, with all their billions in tax-payer provided research money, the NIH wasn't working on a cure for the common cold (instead of all the arcane pursuits I would tell him about). As a journalist and advertising executive, he knew that kind of cure would provide the story—and the sale—of the century. Not to mention save millions of days of lost work and discomfort for Americans.

I had to break it to him that addressing such a "common" concern just wouldn't be in keeping with the "elevated pursuits" and self-opinions of the Mandarins of Medicine at the NIH. Which made him wonder, as a lifelong hard-working man and taxpayer, what exactly we (who pay the bills) are really getting out of all this research at NIH?

I only wish he were still here to see the results of a new study on what may very well be the elusive cure he asked about. Granted, this research didn't, and wouldn't, come from the NIH. But it should finally give many, many people some much needed relief.

As it turns out, the well-known herbal product *Echinacea* can reduce the symptoms and duration of a cold once you catch one.

Of course, Echinacea is well-known these days. It's been a common-sense folk remedy for centuries. And research on it has also been around for a long time. In fact, we published a study showing Echinacea's benefits for colds back in 1994—in the very first issue of the first medical research journal on CAM, which I had founded. And, even then, the results were "nothing to sneeze at."

But this new research should silence the critics and the skeptics once and for all. It's the largest clinical trial on Echinacea ever conducted. The study took place at the Common Cold Center in Cardiff, Wales, and involved 755 people over a period of four months. Those taking Echinacea had fewer colds, of shorter duration, with fewer recurrences of symptoms. The Echinacea treated group also used fewer over-the-counter remedies. And it was effective against influenza viruses as well. And this study is just in time to provide some hope for the flu since both the flu vaccine and the flu treatment, Tamiflu, have now been shown to be victims of more bad science in favor of drug profits.

In addition to being the largest study on Echinacea to-date, it is also the first to track its effectiveness against specific viruses of different varieties. And the fact that it fared so well makes sense, because Echinacea acts by stimulating the immune system to do its job—and get a jump on viruses before they multiply.

We rely on the immune system for combatting all germs—whether they're viral or bacterial. So immune-stimulators like Echinacea are a much better way to tackle infections of any type. Instead of just endlessly searching for antibiotics that are effective against only certain bacteria. Plus, antibiotics don't work at all for the viruses that cause colds and flus.

But Echinacea does. And now the research has become incontrovertible.

The dose used in this study to effectively prevent colds was 2,400 mg per day of a standardized, liquid Echinacea extract. The dose was increased to 4,000 mg per day if a participant came down with cold symptoms. Both doses were effective for their intended purposes. But one helpful hint to keep in mind is if you decide to use Echinacea this winter...

Participants in this study were asked to hold the liquid in their mouths for 10 seconds to ensure it would make direct local contact with any potential viruses in the upper throat.

Chapter 97

Defend against superbugs
with 5 simple steps

Antibiotics can certainly save lives. But their overuse allowed untreatable, antibiotic-resistant superbugs to develop.

One of the deadliest superbugs—called Clostridium difficile (C. difficile)—causes about 250,000 infections and leads to nearly 14,000 deaths each year, according to the Centers for Disease Control (CDC). It also costs the health care system at least $1 billion each year. In a moment, I'll tell you about five steps you can take to defend against C. difficile.

The term C. difficile comes from the Latin word meaning "difficult." And that word certainly applies here. The main symptom with C. difficile is deadly, dehydrating diarrhea (like cholera).

People who take antibiotic drugs are most at risk of getting a C. difficile infection because the drugs wipe out the good bacteria of the normal, healthy microbiome. These good bacteria influence digestion, nutrition, and inflammation, and probably other health factors, in addition to protecting against infectious diarrhea.

Age is also a factor. In fact, according to a new CDC study, one in every three C. difficile infections occurs in people ages 65 years and older. Plus, more than 100,000 cases occur in U.S. nursing homes, spreading from the hands and medical equipment of health professionals. Hospital surfaces are also rife with dangerous bacteria.

Unfortunately, the problem is only getting worse.

In fact, between 2000 and 2010, C. difficile-related hospitalizations doubled. And the rate is still climbing. The CDC attributes part of the dramatic increase to a dangerous new strain of C. difficile called NAP1.

Experts say antibiotics are clearly driving the whole problem. Yet poor detection and diagnostic methods also play a part. For example, in one recent case, a healthy 56-year-old woman developed sudden, painful diarrhea one morning. After a phone consultation, her doctor prescribed the wrong treatment. She went to the emergency room and died less than 36 hours later.

So until the CDC figures out how to turn the tide (don't hold your breath), I suggest you focus on prevention.

Here are some common sense, preventative steps you can take to protect yourself from antibiotic-resistant bacteria. Your choices will also help stem this growing public health problem:

1. **Practice good hygiene.** The simplest step you can take is to wash hands well with regular soap (*not antibacterial agents!*) and water. If you can't get to a wash basin, use alcohol-based hand sanitizers.

2. **Don't take antibiotics** unless you have a bacterial infection that requires treatment with an antibiotic. The best way to determine whether you really need an antibiotic—and which one(s)—is for your doctor to take a sample of the infected area. For example, take a swab of your sore throat and then submit it to the lab to (a) detect the presence of bacteria, (b) determine which bacteria and (c) test to see which antibiotics will work against it. Without taking these steps, it's guesswork.

3. If your doctor determines you *do* have an infection and need an antibiotic, **take the full dose for the full course of treatment**. Up to one-third of the time, patients don't take prescriptions correctly. And inappropriate practices double the use of antibiotics without any clinical benefit whatsoever.

4. **Only choose "organic" meat and dairy** that comes from animals raised without antibiotics.

5. **Keep your immune system in good working order**. This step is probably the single most important thing you can do for your health. Unfortunately, it's also probably the single most overlooked step in fighting deadly "superbugs."

You can keep your immune system healthy by taking a high-quality daily B vitamin complex, 500 mg of vitamin C twice per day, and 10,000 IU of vitamin D daily. Also, get selenium and zinc in your diet from healthy meats and seafood.

You can also boost your immune system when coming down with a cold or flu by taking the herb Echinacea purpurea (purple coneflower).

So while the CDC continues to wring its hands about C. difficile, keep washing yours. And follow my simple, sensible advice for good health and immunity. After all, the best offense we have against deadly superbugs is still a good defense.

PART 9

NATURAL WAYS TO NURTURE YOUR HEALTH

Chapter 98

10 signs you may have low vitamin D

I recommend having your vitamin D levels checked every 12 months through a routine blood test. Your doctor will order the test during your annual check-up. But between visits, and especially at the end of a long, dark winter, you should keep an eye out for 10 signs you may have a vitamin D deficiency. I'll tell you all about those important signs in a moment. But first, let's back up…

As you know, vitamin D is a critical nutrient used by every cell in your body. But an alert *Daily Dispatch* reader informed me that the U.S. Preventive Services Task Force (USPSTF) released a taxpayer-supported report claiming they did not find any evidence supporting the health benefits of supplemental vitamin D.

This report shows exactly what's wrong with healthcare in America. Not only do I *not* trust their findings. I don't trust the bureaucrats who fabricated the report.

These bureaucrats rely on government grants to keep studying the same old questions, using the same old failed approaches. No wonder they never find any solutions. Of course, they don't really want to find any new solutions—because that could put them out of a job or out of a cushy government committee assignment.

The problems start with the flawed and outdated Recommended Daily Allowances (RDAs).

The quasi-government committees that make up the RDAs still focus on preventing 19th century nutritional deficiency diseases. They steadfastly ignore the mounds of scientific evidence published by independent scientists. These well-designed, independent studies support the idea that higher, optimal doses of nutrients can prevent, treat and even cure common diseases.

But the government continues to spend your tax money on regular, ritualistic reviews that use incredibly small doses of vitamins. Then, when the study shows no benefit for the vitamin, they say, *see–that independent study was wrong.*

Today's academic-government-industrial-medical complex will never admit to knowing what the leading natural scientists and philosophers have known for ages—that nutrition is critical for all health and it's involved in all disease.

Though, if they *did* admit this truth, they would find themselves in the company of every genius from Hippocrates to Thomas Sydenham and Thomas Jefferson to Thomas Alva Edison.

But somehow, the bureaucrats believe they know better.

So nothing ever changes—officially.

But, as I said earlier, an incredible amount of scientific evidence supports the need for higher levels of many nutrients for optimal health, including vitamin D.

Actually, the case with vitamin D is even a little different.

You see, with vitamin D, we are not just talking about how higher levels can prevent many common cancers, increase survival time, and improve quality of life in cancer patients. We're not just talking about how higher levels can help prevent heart disease, kidney disease, neurological diseases like multiple sclerosis, and other common problems.

There is, in fact, an actual worldwide deficiency of vitamin D. And evidence links many medical problems with this deficiency.

But government health experts wear blinders when it comes to vitamin D. They still only focus its role in bone health, which is based on discoveries made in the 1920s.

But in the last century, science proved that vitamin D is critical to every cell, tissue and organ in the body—not just the bones.

Medically speaking, there are 10 clear warning signs that you may have a vitamin D deficiency. Doctors see these signs every single day.

1. Bone pain

If you suffer from ongoing bone pain not explained by a "pathologic" diagnosis, you may have low vitamin D.

2. Muscle weakness

Muscles have vitamin D receptors and must have a constant supply to function.

3. Chronic infections and respiratory illnesses

Scientific studies show that vitamin D helps defend against infections and respiratory illnesses, especially in children. In fact, chronic respiratory infections in children are a strong indicator of a vitamin D deficiency. Instead of addressing this issue, the Centers for Disease Control wants all children to get the flu vaccine, which does not prevent the flu and appears to cause a six-fold increase in the risk of respiratory illness.

Thankfully, some doctors are getting the message. In fact, doctors with the prestigious Mayo Clinic advise that you need vitamin D to help your body fight infections. And if you're troubled by frequent infections, they advise getting a vitamin D blood measurement at your doctor's office.

4. Low mood

We know vitamin D helps produce adequate levels of serotonin, a critical neurotransmitter in the brain that produces feelings of well-being. And many solid, independent studies link low vitamin D levels with depression.

Of course, the popular "antidepressant" drugs on the market artificially raise serotonin levels through the roundabout way of preventing its re-uptake from the synapses.

Unfortunately, these selective serotonin reuptake inhibitors (SSRIs) only work in one out seven patients. And new research suggests the one patient who *does* feel better after taking the SSRI probably *only* does so because of a placebo effect. Not because the drug actually works.

Plus, SSRIs cause a wide range of harmful side effects.

Evidence links low vitamin D with increased anxiety, which frequently accompanies depression. Aside from clinical conditions like anxiety or depression, vitamin D's effect on serotonin can impact mood in anybody. So if your mood is off, it may be a sign of vitamin D deficiency.

5. Abnormal sweating

Abnormal sweating can be a sign of vitamin D deficiency. In fact, years ago, doctors commonly asked pregnant mothers if they experienced heavy sweating, since nutritional deficiency can occur under the strenuous demands of a growing baby.

6. Congestive heart failure

Maintaining sufficient vitamin D is a long-term, lifetime proposition. And if you don't maintain adequate levels over your lifetime, it even affects your heart muscle. In fact, the National Institutes of Health now recognizes scientific studies that show vitamin D deficiency can lead to congestive heart failure.

7. High blood pressure

Researchers link high blood pressure, a major cause of heart disease, with low vitamin D. In fact, a prospective study on women conducted by Harvard University over many years found that women with low vitamin D had 66 percent higher risk of high blood pressure compared to women with the highest levels of D.

8. Chronic pain

Studies show low vitamin D levels increase the risk of suffering from chronic pain. In fact, general malaise or fatigue may also be associated with lack of vitamin D. In athletes, lack of endurance may be a sign of low vitamin D levels.

9. Skin conditions

Your skin improves with moderate sun exposure. And studies show you can improve a variety of common skin conditions—such as dermatitis and eczema—by supplementing with vitamin D. In fact, many forward-thinking doctors now use vitamin D therapy to treat psoriasis patients. Plus, according to the Mayo Clinic, no matter what treatment is used, psoriasis is harder to manage unless vitamin D levels are adequate.

10. Kidney problems

Vitamin D is also important for the kidneys, which help make the active form of vitamin D in the body. So if you have kidney disease caused by cardiovascular disease or diabetes, low vitamin D contributes to this vicious cycle. Simply getting older can make it harder for you to get enough vitamin D. The body just doesn't activate as much of it as you age. Of course, most the medical conditions I mentioned above also become more common with age. So while vitamin D is important throughout your life, it's especially important as you get older. Which is why it's critical to stay vigilant. Be on the lookout for any of the telltale symptoms listed above. And again, have your levels checked annually. The ideal vitamin D level for optimal health is 30 ng/ml or more.

To reach and maintain this optimal level, make sure to supplement with 5,000 IU of vitamin D daily. If you don't like taking pills, you can get vitamin D in a liquid form, which is now available together with astaxanthin, which you can take straight on the tongue or add to a small glass of natural fruit juice or milk in the morning.

Chapter 99

Avoid antibiotics, fight gum disease, and more with the all-natural little blue wonder

We already know blueberries are helpful for memory and cognition, and research shows they also help protect against cardiovascular disease, diabetes, and obesity. Research has even uncovered the beneficial effects of blueberries on dental health and reducing the use of antibiotics.

It's quite an extensive array of benefits, considering this berry has only recently come under scientific scrutiny.

Wild blueberries are three times better for you than farm-grown fruit

There are two major types of blueberries that grow in the U.S. The low-bush blueberry, which is the wild variety (*Vaccinium angustifolium*) and a high-bush variety. High bush blueberries have been cultivated to grow at a higher elevation than wild blueberries would typically grow in their rocky native soil.

Blueberries are rich sources of phenolic acids, which have both antioxidant and anti-inflammatory properties.

Of course, the reason that plants produce bioactive phenols and other constituents is to protect them under the strenuous conditions of the wild. Cultivated plants have it "easy" by comparison and need to produce far fewer phenolic and other bioactive compounds for their growth and protection.

Research shows that total phenolic content is over three times higher in the wild compared to the cultivated varieties. Which means wild blueberries are three times better for your health.

Beyond phenols, there are many other constituents in blueberries that contribute to their total antioxidant capacity.

For instance, blueberries also have abundant anthocyanins, which give them their characteristic dark blue color. Like phenols, anthocyanins have anti-inflammatory properties and act as natural antioxidants.

Heart benefits that rival pharmaceutical drugs

One study looked at the benefits of blueberry anthocyanins at protecting the linings of blood vessels from damage.

Blueberries have also been studied for their ability to prevent atherosclerosis, or hardening of the arteries.

One study looked at the effects of wild blueberry powder on **fat accumulation in white blood cells** — which is one of the culprits in atherosclerosis.

The researchers found that even low concentrations of blueberry anthocyanins reduced fat accumulation. And two other blueberry components—syringic and gallic acid—were also found to be effective at lowering fat accumulation in white blood cells.

Best of all, the concentrations of blueberry anthocyanins found to be effective in these studies are readily achievable in your everyday diet with proper supplementation.

Another clinical trial showed that daily blueberry consumption improved **blood pressure** and **arterial stiffness** in postmenopausal women suffering from early-stage high blood pressure.

The study involved 48 participants who received either 22 grams of freeze-dried blueberry powder or 22 grams of a placebo powder daily. After eight weeks, the blueberry group's blood pressure was significantly lower. Systolic pressure dropped from 138 to 131 mmHg, and diastolic pressure dropped from 80 to 75 mmHg.

An effect that significant may very well allow older individuals to opt for blueberry supplements instead of blood pressure drugs to treat hypertension.

Biochemical measurements were also done on the study participants. The women who ate blueberries had increased production of nitrous oxide, a very powerful relaxant of blood vessels. Basically, nitrous oxide widens the vessels and reduces blood pressure, while supplying good blood circulation to the brain and other tissues.

To recap, in terms of cardiovascular benefits, research shows that blueberries do it all—reducing the oxidation and inflammation that damage blood vessels, curtailing the accumulation of fats that causes atherosclerosis in damaged arteries, and lowering blood pressure and arterial stiffness—which are both major factors for heart disease.

But the benefits of blueberries don't stop with the heart.

The new "brain food"

Other research shows that whole, fresh, high-bush blueberries (*Vaccinium corymbosum*) help reduce the **oxidative stress** that can lead to **age-related brain damage**.

In one study, lab animals that ate blueberries were protected from oxidation and destruction of brain cells. And their brain tissue was actually able to repair damage due to age-related changes.

Biochemical measurements also demonstrated that blueberries supported antioxidant activity in a number of the animals' cellular functions. In addition, key neurotransmitter activity was increased in the animals' brain and nervous tissues.

Tiny berries offer big immune benefits

For the immune system, one study showed that six weeks of daily ingestion of blueberry powder **increased natural killer cells** (T cell counts) in sedentary men and women. These white blood cells are key to protecting the body from infections, cancer, and other diseases. My colleague Dr. Jerry Thornthwaite discovered natural killer cells back in the 1970s, and their importance continues to be uncovered.

Blueberries may also be an unexpected weapon in the war against obesity and diabetes.

Based on the research I reported above about reducing fat accumulation, you might be wondering if blueberries have a role in preventing obesity. Indeed, scientific research shows blueberry anthocyanins can help **prevent weight gain, support weight loss, and help prevent the metabolic complications of obesity like diabetes.**

When certain white blood cells (macrophages) infiltrate fat tissue, they contribute to complications like type 2 diabetes. But anthocyanin-rich fractions from blueberries were found to reduce inflammation and fat tissue formation in one study.

These compounds also restored insulin and glucose uptake of fat tissue.

Wild blueberry consumption also showed benefits regarding glucose metabolism in a lab animal model of metabolic syndrome and diabetes.

The important advice your dentist won't give you

Latest research demonstrates how blueberries can help fight **gum disease** (periodontitis) and also **reduce the use of antibiotics**.

Gum disease can result when dental bacteria build up plaque on teeth, causing the gums to become inflamed. Researchers found that wild blueberry extract (remember, wild blueberry is about three times more potent than domestic) helps prevent dental plaque formation, providing a new natural therapy for periodontitis and reducing the need for antibiotics.

Blueberry polyphenols have already been shown to work against foodborne disease-causing bacteria, so the scientists tested whether they also fight a microbe called Fusobacterium, which is one of the main culprits in periodontitis.

In the lab, they tested extracts from the wild, low-bush blueberry and found they inhibit growth of this bacteria and its ability to form plaque. The blueberry extracts also blocked a molecular pathway involved in causing inflammation.

The researchers believe the best approach would be to develop a special oral device to slowly release blueberry extract into the mouth and onto the teeth after deep dental cleaning. But you don't necessarily have to wait for development and FDA approval of expensive treatments with new device, or a trip to the dentist for an unpleasant deep cleaning.

Blueberry extract is available in a water-soluble, powdered form that can be added to any beverage. It's designed to be swallowed so it can be absorbed in the blood and tissues. But you can also hold the beverage in your mouth for a while to savor the flavor before swallowing—and do some good for your teeth and gums too.

Look for a dietary supplement or water-soluble powder containing 400 mg of blueberry extract.

Chapter 100

African "tree of life" yields a nutritional gold mine—proving this is one superfood worthy of the title

Every other week it seems something new is being touted as the next "superfood." So it's hard to take the claims seriously. But when it comes to baobab, there's plenty of truth behind the hype. Making it a true "superfood" worthy of your attention.

The fruit, leaves, and seeds of this massive tree have more vitamin C than oranges. More calcium than milk. More antioxidants than strawberries.

Plus, baobab fruit is packed with minerals like magnesium—which is essential for everything from heart to bone health.

If you've never heard of baobab (pronounced bay-oh-bab), that's because it's virtually impossible to find the fruit in the U.S. But the good news is that you can now get the benefits of this healthful fruit without having to travel all the way to Africa.

How one massive tree provides such an abundance of sustenance?

In Africa, baobab is known as the "tree of life." Fitting, since some of these massive trees are thought to be up to 6,000 years old.

Baobab grows throughout the woodlands, grasslands, and savannahs of sub-Saharan Africa. It can reach heights of 75 feet, and its roots can spread even further.

African communities rely on the whole tree for their daily existence. The cork-like bark is used to make cloth and rope. The trunk stores water during times of drought. The leaves are used in traditional medicines. And the coconut-sized fruit is both tasty and nutritious.

And here's the impressive amount of nutrients in this "tree of life."

Calcium. Research shows that baobab leaves are very rich in calcium—between 1,500 to 2,250 mg in every 100 grams. Only amaranth, okra, onion leaves, and sorrel provide better plant-based sources of calcium. And the same amount of whole milk only has 113 mg of this essential mineral.

Vitamin C. Baobab fruit pulp has between 150 to 500 mg of this disease-fighting vitamin per 100 grams. How does that stack up to other food sources of C? Well, oranges only have 53 mg, kiwis have 93 mg, and yellow bell peppers have 184 mg.

Magnesium. Baobab pulp has an average of 195 mg of magnesium per 100 grams. In contrast, magnesium-rich foods like dark leafy greens have 79 mg. Mackerel has 97 mg. Only squash and pumpkin seeds have more magnesium than baobab.

Antioxidants. Baobab's antioxidant levels are (almost) off the charts. One gram of baobab fruit pulp has an integral antioxidant capacity (IAC) reading of 11, and the leaves have an IAC of 9. Check out how that compares to the IACs of popular high-antioxidant fruits: strawberries (1), kiwi (0.3), apple (0.2), and orange (0.1).

Polyphenols. Baobab is loaded with these disease-fighting compounds. In fact, one study showed that baobab extract mixed into water helped people digest dietary starch better—and reduced their blood glucose levels. Which suggests that baobab may be effective at helping fight diabetes. Other studies have revealed that the fruit has potent anti-inflammatory effects.

And the above list is just the beginning… research also shows baobab is a good source of manganese, phosphorus, potassium, and zinc. It also has A and B vitamins and lutein—which is essential for eye health.

So how can you benefit from this tree of life?

As I mentioned earlier, you're not likely to find the actual baobab fruit in your produce section. Unfortunately it just doesn't travel well. So most Americans can't sit down to a menu of dishes made from baobab leaves or fruit.

However, baobab is now more readily available as a powdered ingredient. And can be found as a dietary supplement. A combination of dried baobab powder with other supplement ingredients can provide a potent addition to your daily regimen.

I recommend 500-1,000 mg per day.

Since the optimal quantities of baobab don't really fit into a pill or capsule, the best form is a water-soluble powder. Mix the powder with water, tea, or juice, and you'll get a health boost you'll never achieve with sports drinks, so-called "hydration" drinks, or energy drinks.

Chapter 101

The single most important thing you can do to prevent premature death

As the U.S. government science bureaucrats continue dithering over recommendations about vitamin D intake, some real scientists in Germany (and yes, even some right here at home) are making it perfectly clear: Vitamin D prevents premature death. Plus, it reduces death rates from all causes.

So why is the U.S. hemming and hawing—and confusing patients and doctors alike?

Blind leading the blind

Over the past three decades, many scientists who study chronic diseases have stumbled into studying diet and nutrition. They often lack any understanding of nutrition as a fundamental part of human biology and behavior. And despite their ignorance on matters of nutrition, they publish their findings. And the government science bureaucrats jump on the research—and the politically correct bandwagon.

But one source has always been an exception to the rule. *The American Journal of Clinical Nutrition* (AJCN) doesn't report spurious statistical findings like those that can be found in other journals.

And across the Atlantic, German scientists tend to put out reliable information on nutrition. That's because they know how to conduct scientific investigations on human biology. They have consistently been way ahead of the United States in investigating natural and nutritional approaches to health and medicine.

Research you can trust

The trustworthy team at AJCN published a report in their April 2013 issue that takes a close look at vitamin D.

In it, a team of scientists measured vitamin D levels in nearly 10,000 people ages 50 to 74 years. Another 5,500 participants were measured at 5 year-follow-up. All deaths were recorded during an average follow-up period of 9.5 years. During the follow-up period about 10 percent of study participants died: 43.3 percent from cancer, 35.0 percent from heart disease, and 5.5 percent of respiratory diseases.

People with the lowest vitamin D levels were more likely to have died of any cause, and of cancer, heart disease, and respiratory disease specifically.

They also found a dose-response relationship between low vitamin D levels and death—that is, the lower the vitamin D, the higher the mortality rate.

This is the best kind of epidemiological study, with the strongest kind of results that can be performed on human populations. It makes it perfectly clear: Higher vitamin D levels protect against premature death—as well as all the leading causes of death.

It's never too late to up your D

Plenty of studies prove the dangerous effects of lack of vitamin D in childhood, but these highlight the fact that even in adults—and older adults at that—low levels of D have bad health effects.

On the flip side, that means that even later in life, you can improve your health and longevity by increasing your vitamin D intake.

And here's some more good news: Vitamin D can be free. All you need to do is expose your skin to the sun and your body will activate its own vitamin D.

During the Fall and Winter months you can build up healthy vitamin D levels with appropriate high-quality supplements. If you have any reason to believe you are not getting enough vitamin D, ask your doctor to measure your levels the next time you have a routine blood sample taken for testing. If you're below 75 nmol/L—and especially below 30 nmol/L—it's time to add a high-quality supplement.

Chapter 102

Today's TRUE nutrient deficiencies

Fourteen years ago, two landmark studies were published in the *Journal of the American Medical Association (JAMA)*. They revealed that the dietary standards set by the U.S. government are grossly inadequate.

These two studies should have changed the way doctors viewed the role of optimal nutrition in preventing and treating chronic diseases.

Yet, here we are—over a decade later. And the government recommended dietary allowances (RDAs) are still the only benchmark conventional doctors acknowledge and recommend.

The information on nutrition and health that the public is given (and not given) by the government sometimes reminds me of the book *Catch-22* by Joseph Heller. Really one scene in particular that depicts an aviator being hit by anti-aircraft flak. The protagonist, Yossarian (Alan Arkin in the movie), labors carefully to bandage the relatively superficial wounds on the injured flyer's arms and legs. Yet, when he finishes, he opens the flyer's heavy flight jacket only to find his intestines spilling out through a fatal abdominal wound.

Bloody and graphic, yes. But not that far off from how the government handles its RDAs. Follow them, and we're all like poor, well-intentioned Yossarian. Applying Band-Aids to potentially fatal health problems.

The government guidelines on nutrient intakes are hopelessly outdated.

They were designed to prevent frank vitamin and nutritional deficiencies. And diseases like beri-beri, kwashiorkor, pellagra, rickets, and scurvy.

So yes, the government is keeping us safe from some deadly scourges— *of the 19th century*. But what about what's killing us in the 21st century?

Will they ever move on to the true nutritional medicine proposed 10 years ago in those landmark *JAMA* articles?

Government RDAs don't even come close

In those old *JAMA* articles, the researchers gathered more than 150 studies. And after carefully examining all the data, they determined just how much of several common vitamins most people need each day to help prevent today's chronic diseases. Including heart disease, cancer, diabetes and osteoporosis, as well as infectious diseases.

But, in many cases, what they found was vastly different from even the most current government RDAs.

Take a look at the chart at the end of this chapter, which shows the current RDA of several specific nutrients, compared to the optimal amounts determined by the *JAMA* articles back in 2002.

Obviously, the government is still hopelessly out of touch with what the human body really needs for optimal health.

One step forward, two steps back

Today the government does (finally) recognize that vitamin D deficiency is a serious problem—even by their standards. Current estimates show that up to 30 percent of the population isn't getting the RDA. But the true dimensions of the worldwide vitamin D deficiency epidemic are likely a lot higher from the standpoint of optimal nutrition. Meanwhile, at the same time, they tell everyone to avoid sun exposure, which is critical for achieving and maintaining even the RDA vitamin D levels. (For the record, you should aim for 15-20 minutes of direct sun exposure—on the arms and legs—per day, at least three times per week. *Without* sunscreen.)

The government also continues to dwell on nutritional "problems" that don't really exist. For example, they still focus on iron deficiency as a "major" public health issue. (Despite the fact that it occurs only in 11 to 16 percent of *some* subgroups of children and child-bearing women.) Granted, they now recognize that their old iron measurement techniques leave a lot to be desired. Of course, they haven't done anything about their standards.

And one troubling new development that no one is currently talking about is the prevalence of iodine deficiency—especially in young women. We thought we had that problem ended by adding iodine to our salt supply. But with the CDC constantly telling people to lower their salt intake (to potentially dangerously low levels at that), it's really no wonder this problem has emerged.

The best way to get everything you need for optimal health

Those landmark *JAMA* articles also pointed out, as I have for 30 years, that the stand-alone nutrients recognized by the RDAs actually fall short in yet another way when it comes to helping you get the optimal nutrition you need…

You see, on their own, these vitamins don't include the other critical nutritional components in healthy foods and vegetables (like lycopene and lutein, for instance).

It stands to reason that plants, which thrive outdoors, must have some built-in protection from the elements. Indeed, they've developed antioxidants to protect them from oxidation and "free radicals" that are inevitable parts of constant exposure to oxygen in the atmosphere and to regular climatic events.

So eating a nutritious, balanced diet is truly the only way to get all the biologically-active and beneficial compounds you need for optimal health, whether the RDAs recognize them or not.

Of course, I don't mean to diminish the importance of those RDA nutrients. It's just that you'll get even more benefits if you opt for whole foods that contain them. Because these food sources also offer other benefits that still aren't even on the government's RDA radar screen yet.

The following is a chart comparing the current government RDA and the optimal amount of nutrients you truly need.

Nutrient	Current government RDA	Optimal amount (via 2002 JAMA articles)
Folate	400 micrograms	800 micrograms
Vitamin A	3,000 IU for men 2,333 IU for women	15,000 IU
Vitamin B6	1.3 milligrams for adults up to 50 1.7 milligrams for men over 50 1.5 milligrams for women over 50	3 milligrams
Vitamin B12	2.4 micrograms	9 micrograms
Vitamin C	90 milligrams for men 75 milligrams for women	2,000 milligrams
Vitamin D	600 IU	2,000 IU (but safe in doses up to 30,000 IU)
Vitamin E	15 milligrams	70 milligrams

Here are the best food sources for the RDA nutrients listed in the chart above.

Folate: dark green, leafy vegetables (like broccoli, Brussels sprouts, cabbage, kale, spinach); asparagus; avocados; bananas; beans; oranges; yeast

Vitamin A: organ meats, fish, shellfish, egg yolks, fruits and vegetables (some carotenoids in fruits and vegetables are converted to vitamin A in the body)

Vitamin B6: poultry, fish, shellfish, soybeans, bananas, nuts, peas

Vitamin B12: poultry, fish, meat, eggs

Vitamin C: broccoli, citrus fruits, melons, peppers, strawberries, tomatoes

Vitamin D: saltwater fish, fish liver oil, liver, fortified milk (and while it's not a food, don't forget about a critical source of vitamin D: sunshine)

Vitamin E: nuts, vegetable oils, wheat germ

One quick note for vegetarians and vegans. Take another look above at vitamins A, B6, B12, and D. Most of these key nutrients come from animal sources. Unfortunately, the average human just can't get optimal nutrition from a diet that doesn't include meat. So vegetarians and vegans should always take high-quality supplements to achieve optimal levels.

Getting to the "guts" of the problem

Unfortunately, the government is no closer today to giving people truly sound nutritional advice than they were a decade ago. Like poor, misguided Yossarian from *Catch-22*, the "experts" can't seem to get at the real "guts" of the problem.

I remember exchanging communications a few years ago with one of the leading Ph.D. nutritional experts at Johns Hopkins in Baltimore. He's a very influential figure in the American Society for Clinical Nutrition and plays a big role in helping determine the RDAs. I asked him flat out why he still didn't accept that optimal nutrient intakes need to be higher than the established RDAs. He responded simply, "There is no evidence."

By what standard?

Maybe he and his colleagues haven't been reading the *Journal of the American Medical Association* for the past 10+ years.

But if we wait for all the evidence sought by some of these non-medical, Ph.D., career scientists we'll all be dead. Probably from some preventable disease.

The evidence is here—and has been for over a decade. So do yourself, and your health, a favor and forget about the "bare minimum" RDAs. Instead, strive for optimal nutrition.

Focus your diet on the foods listed above, and fill in any gaps with good, high-quality nutritional supplements.

Chapter 103

The dangerous delusion of "detox" drinks

Here we go again…A tried and true tenet of natural healing is being potentially misunderstood by mainstream medicine and meanwhile exploited by the quick-fix (and quick-buck) "health" marketeers.

This time it's with the delusion of so-called "detox" products and drinks. But unfortunately, the detox-in-a-blender fad bears no resemblance to any authentic detox regimen.

What is detox, anyway?

Some of the new drink marketeers may not know it, but it actually stands for detoxification. And that can mean two very different things from a health perspective:

1. To the medical establishment, it's about appropriate treatment for drug or alcohol intoxication or addiction.

2. In natural medicine, it's a way of restoring the body, mind, and spirit to their most cleansed, balanced and healthful state.

The characters running around promoting "detox" drinks (who seem hyped up on their own adrenaline) could use a good detox themselves. They need to slow down, and take time (and even lie down) for an authentic, natural detox treatment…as I'll demonstrate in just a moment.

Heavy metals and other "toxins"

A really unfortunate thing about the wildly incorrect messages about detox is that real detoxification is an important cornerstone of good health. It's something we should all do periodically to get rid of toxic accumulations that slow down our bodies and cloud our minds.

The human body accumulates toxins, like heavy metals, that the liver can't effectively metabolize and the kidney can't adequately excrete. Metals like **lead** or excess **iron** can accumulate and poison virtually any and all tissues of the body. Fortunately, there is a real medical treatment for effectively eliminating lead that I will tell you about shortly. Other toxins, including chemicals from pesticides, for example, accumulate in body fat.

Note to dieters: One of many reasons I recommend slow, steady weight loss is that accumulated toxic chemicals trapped in fat tissues are released into the blood and body when fat is metabolized due to caloric restriction. A sudden release of toxins into the bloodstream can temporarily poison other tissues in the body, causing symptoms that may convince you that your weight loss is doing more harm than good, at least temporarily.

But back to the medical treatment I mentioned for eliminating excess lead from the body. Chelation therapy using infusion with a substance called EDTA has been approved for use by the FDA for lead poisoning. The EDTA chemically traps the heavy metal so it can be eliminated in the urine. After many years of study, research recently established that chelation therapy with EDTA, together with vitamin C, is effective for treating and reversing cardiovascular disease.

Mainstream medical "experts" were quick to claim it was the vitamin C—not the chelation therapy itself—that was responsible for the positive effect. (Yes, these are indeed the same "experts who are usually quick to claim that vitamins have <u>no </u>effect on heart disease, or anything else, for that matter!)

Is your body poisoning itself?

"Alternative" or natural medicine holds that everyday food consumption results in toxic buildup. The idea is that when we break down the food's constituents and our gut bacteria carry out their own metabolism, the result is that we produce chemical products that are "foreign" to the body—termed "auto-intoxication."

This is a 19th century concept that we now realize is more complex in terms of the microbiome and the role of probiotics and fiber.

Modern research validates genuine detoxification

Some of my own research in the late 20th century actually validated some of the 19th century ideas about auto-intoxication. Based on a theory from Dr. Nicholas Petrakis at University of California, San Francisco, I performed an analysis with colleagues at the National Cancer Institute (NCI) on the US National Health and Nutrition Examination Survey.

We found that less frequent bowel movements (constipation) in women is related to higher rates of breast cancer.

Dr. Petrakis thought that constipation allowed toxic, carcinogenic breakdown products to accumulate in the intestines, which would then be absorbed back into the blood and could cause cancer in tissues. We found such results for the most common cancer in women. But we were quietly told by our political bosses at NCI not to pursue this research because nobody really believed in those old ideas anymore... despite the evidence we had just found.

Change your body and your life with true detoxification

So far I've covered two types of detoxification: alcohol/drug detox and removal of heavy metals and chemicals from the body. But it's the cleansing of this "auto-intoxication" that applies to the vast majority of us.

What I hope you take away from this is that the true detoxification, or cleansing, that I'm about to describe, can change your body and your life. All those ways in which you feel sluggish, "stuck," or foggy—this type of detoxification can reverse them.

But here's the thing: You'll have to slow down and take your time to reap the rewards (in fact, the slowing down is a reward in itself). *This detox does not come in a bottle.* Rest and relaxation, good air, pure water, and "energy" form the foundation of any authentic detox.

This approach is bound to be good for whatever ails you.

Ancient detoxification rituals get new life

The idea of accumulated toxins actually goes back before the 19th century—*way before*.

Ayurveda, the 5,000-year-old healing system of India, recognizes toxic buildup, and that's why purification plays such a crucial role in Ayurvedic medicine. The difference is that while Western natural medicine is concerned with *products of digestion*, Ayurveda places emphasis on the toxic effects of poorly or *undigested food* (or thoughts, or experiences—all known as *ama*).

Did you notice I referred to "purification," and not "detoxification"? Rather than thinking of the process as "de-" anything, Ayurveda takes a more positive approach. The mainstay of Ayurvedic purification is an intensive treatment regimen that's custom tailored to each individual based on constitution, season, medical or emotional conditions, and other factors.

Panchakarma (PK), or "five actions," is not a just a quick "do-it-yourself" detox in a bottle. It requires the help of an Ayurvedic practitioner, who will design a program just for you. The program entails a customized, combination herbal remedy, modified diet of easily digestible foods, a schedule that honors nature's daily cycles, and daily treatments performed by highly trained therapists. PK can last anywhere from a few days to more than a month. Some facilities offer outpatient services, but many people choose to stay at the treatment center so they can focus without distraction on the intense purification they're undergoing.

And the treatments? While they're not quite like what you'll experience at a typical spa, they are incredibly relaxing and balancing. Well— most of them anyway.

Some of the actions of PK are not practiced in the west because they're somewhat extreme and unpleasant. One, the *basti*, or enema, is frequently included as a substitute, but may not constitute what you might consider a typical day at the spa. But together with the PK's heat-based massages, aromatherapy, and stimulating treatments, it creates a purification experience like no other.

While PK is based on age-old understanding of toxic buildup, it may address the more modern variety as well. Preliminary research has shown that its treatments can mobilize and remove toxic, fat-soluble pesticides and agrochemicals from the body.

So as you can see, an authentic detox is nothing like downing an energy drink (which the FDA is now warning are actually toxic themselves). A major benefit to following any of the authentic, natural approaches is that they make you slow down and take time to focus, relax, and rejuvenate. No one has figured out how to put that in a bottle just yet.

As former Surgeon General Dr. C. Everett Koop used to tell me, sometimes the "tincture of time" is the best medicine of all.

If you need help finding an Ayurvedic practitioner near you, try the National Ayurvedic Medical Association at www.ayurvedanama.org. Their website has a directory of practitioners.

Chapter 104

7 sneaky foods that pretend to be healthy

Every day, people choose foods that seem healthy but really aren't. Here's a look at seven of these sneaky "health" foods.

#1: Banana chips. These snacks are made from a fruit that is naturally high in potassium—and fruits and vegetables are generally healthy foods. But just like their unhealthy potato chip cousins, banana chips are deep fried in high-calorie oil.

Just half a cup of banana chips can have around 200 calories and 10 grams of saturated fat.

Meanwhile, a large, fresh banana is virtually fat free and contains only about 120 calories. Plus, it has more vitamins and minerals than banana chips, because frying can destroy vital nutrients. If you like bananas, you're much better off sticking with the whole, uncooked fruit.

#2: Energy bars. You can find energy bars sneaked into the grocery aisle with healthy foods, or even in the weight-loss section. But beware. Many of these crazed concoctions average 200 to 250 calories each. And since most energy bars tend to be small, it's not unusual to down a couple a day as a supposedly nutritious "snack."

But then you find that you've eaten as many calories as you'd get in a healthy, large lunch or moderate dinner. In that sense, energy bars are meal "replacements," with all of the calories (and more) but few of the nutrients—and none of the enjoyment, satisfaction, or benefits of eating a real meal.

The sugar content can also be quite high, accounting for many of energy bars' empty calories, and making some of them no better than candy bars. And they're not even as tasty.

If you need a portable, "on-the-go" snack, try a hard-boiled egg or a fresh banana.

#3: Muesli. This is a health food store staple and hard to pronounce, so it must be good for you, right?

Muesli is marketed as a healthy alternative to sugary breakfast cereals. And while there are some brands that have fewer than 200 calories per serving, there are others that have a whopping 600 calories per cup—with high fat content and ridiculous amounts of added sugar, to boot.

If you like having some sort of cereal in the morning, you can make your own healthy version. Buy bulk oats, sunflower seeds, dried fruits (cut into small bits), and some nuts, mix them together, and add milk. Alternately, eggs are a great, nutritious way to start the day.

#4: Prepared salads. There is nothing healthier than a fresh, green salad. But when you order a salad at a restaurant, watch out for the extra calories, fat, and sugar often used to dress it up so it tastes better.

If you trust the basic ingredients, ask for the dressing on the side. Or ask for olive oil and vinegar (or lemon) and dress your own salad at the table. And of course, you can also make these dressings at home. Don't ever buy or use prepared salad dressings. To keep your olive oil fresh, only buy as much as you will use in a three-month period.

#5: Sushi. This trendy food is bound to be good for you, right? After all, what could be healthier than raw fish (even if you're not a seal)?

While the nutrient content of sushi is indeed healthy, any uncooked food can pose a risk of infection or infestation with parasites. Although the high standards of real sushi restaurants present a minimal risk, watch out for the proliferation of "sushi-on-the-side" eateries where chefs aren't well versed in proper sushi preparation.

You also need to be careful of mercury contamination. Mercury is common in fish, and because many of the fish used in sushi are large predators at the top of the marine food chain, they can have high concentrations of mercury.

Tuna is particularly problematic. Some experts say adults should avoid eating more than 6 ounces of tuna sushi per week to make sure they don't consume too much mercury. And pregnant women and children should eat even less.

#6: Low-fat yogurt. I have often warned that many of the processed foods labeled as "low-fat" contain extra sugar to make them taste better. And studies are showing this added sugar—*not* naturally occurring fat—is the real culprit behind many chronic diseases.

You are better off with a real, full-fat yogurt. Real yogurt is made from milk, which we all know is a good source of calcium and vitamins A and D. It also contains beneficial bacteria (probiotics) that digest the sugar found in milk and thus naturally lower yogurt's sugar content.

#7: Trail mix. We have now reached the end of the unhealthy food trail. Which seems appropriate because trail mix, while supposedly nutritious, may be the sneakiest snack of all.

A basic trail mix made solely of dried fruits and nuts is a good, healthy snack. Nuts and fruits eaten in moderation are natural, high-nutrient foods. In fact, they form a basis of the "Bear Diet," which I recommend for healthy weight loss and weight maintenance.

But prepackaged trail mixes typically contain lots of "tasty" ingredients like milk chocolate candies, sugar-coated nuts, yogurt-covered raisins, corn syrup, and fried banana chips. These ingredients are packed with refined sugars, and can boost the calorie content of a trail mix to a whopping 44 calories *per tablespoon*. That's more than 700 calories per cup!

This caloric load can also include a hefty amount of trans-fats, which should be completely banned from any diet (and are finally being banned by the FDA over the next couple of years).

The alternative is to make your own trail mix with nuts and dried berries from your health food store. Not only will you save a lot of money and calories, but you'll also have a very nutritious snack that you can eat anywhere, whether you're waiting in traffic or scaling the Sierra Nevada Mountains.

Why nuts and berries? Nuts are high in vitamins and minerals and are associated with a lower risk of heart disease, high blood pressure, diabetes, metabolic syndrome, cancer, gallstones, and obesity. Berries have been linked to a lower risk of cancer, cardiovascular disease, and urinary tract infections. They also boost immune function.

And if that weren't impressive enough, nuts and berries together are an antioxidant and immune-system powerhouse. The combo also shows benefits for brain and nerve function. A growing number of clinical studies demonstrate that moderate consumption of berries and nuts improves cognitive performance. The dynamic duo may also delay, or even reverse, the effects of age-related dementia.

The truth is, eating healthy doesn't have to be a guessing game.

A little common sense goes a long way. And when in doubt, you can't go wrong by always opting for whole, natural foods over processed, prepackaged products—no matter how sneakily nutritious they may seem.

Chapter 105

7 simple food-safety tips to keep you and your family healthy

We hear a lot of horror stories about outbreaks of foodborne illnesses. And that can make you wonder whether any fruit, vegetable, meat, or dairy you buy is really safe—even if it's organic.

But while the media make it seem like foodborne illnesses are on the rise, the CDC reports that actually isn't the case. In 1999, the CDC estimated there were about 76 million cases of foodborne illnesses each year in the U.S., resulting in 325,000 hospitalizations and 5,000 deaths. In 2011, those numbers dropped to 48 million cases, with 128,000 hospitalizations and 3,000 deaths.

That's still a shocking number of food safety incidents, but the good news is that the vast majority of cases are mild.

Still, the crony-capitalist government never wants to let a good crisis go to waste, and lobbyists have influenced new "food safety" legislation to actually hide provisions that favor big food and agriculture—and take away control from small farmers and consumers.

But you can still avoid some of these big-government intrusions in the name of "food safety." Just buy locally grown foods. Foods sold within 50 miles of their points of origin are not subject to some of the most restrictive and ridiculous regulations of the FDA and USDA. Most grocery stores of all sizes and descriptions now have sections for locally grown foods. Ask your grocer.

Knowing where and how your food is grown goes a long way toward helping protect you and your family from foodborne illnesses. But there are also other steps you can take. Here are my top recommendations to keep you and your family safe from E. coli, salmonella, listeria, and other bacteria linked to foodborne illnesses.

Don't automatically assume meat is the culprit

Often when we hear about E. coli and salmonella outbreaks, it may actually be due to contaminated produce—not meat (although big government sometimes confuses the facts).

Case in point: the recent E. coli outbreaks at Chipotle restaurants.

There's a theory that big food and agriculture corporations were threatened by this large food chain's popularity and commitment to using clean, organic ingredients. But despite talk that the meat used in Chipotle's menu items was responsible for the outbreaks, it may have really been the lettuce. And the theory is that the lettuce may have been purposefully infected with E. coli by Chipotle's rivals.

Whether or not this this is true, the bottom line is that the Chipotle outbreak was most likely not caused by meat. Indeed, despite the fact that the politically correct love to jump onto the anti-meat bandwagon whenever possible, themajority of foodborne illness outbreaks are not from meat.

Like the case of Chipotle, they're actually caused by contaminated produce. Which leads me to my next point...

Wash produce—even (and especially) if it's bagged

You need to wash all produce before you eat it, even if you think it's been washed before. And don't be fooled by bagged produce claiming to be "triple washed."

Some of the largest salmonella outbreaks have been due to bagged lettuce. And in January, there were listeria outbreaks throughout the U.S. due to bagged lettuce produced at a Dole facility.

That's why the simplest way to protect yourself from deadly bacteria is to neverbuy bagged produce.

Why? Well, bagged produce claims to be "ready to eat," but that doesn't mean it's safe. Much of this produce is washed but not sanitized. And conventional bagged produce may be "washed" with dangerous chemicals.

You won't run into that with organic produce, but I still don't recommend eating any type of packaged vegetables or fruits. Not only because of the potential microbial contamination, but because I think it's a good idea to avoid all packaged foods.

After all, why package a healthy food like greens? It's wasteful and unnatural. Not to mention that there have been reports that some lettuce can be two weeks old before it's even stuck in a bag.

That's why I always recommend buying your produce in bulk from the grocery store or farmer's market, where you can inspect it without the camouflage of a plastic bag. And you can wash it yourself.

The CDC recommends washing all produce under running water at room temperature (using a soft brush to remove any stubborn dirt). If the water is too hot or cold, it can open up pores in fruits and vegetables that could trap bacteria and other contaminants.

Cook meat at the right temperature to kill bacteria

While you're busy washing your produce, you might be wondering if you should also wash your meat and poultry before cooking it.

Don't!

Salmonella bacteria are frequently present on chicken, but rinsing poultry simply contaminates your sink. And that can spread salmonella to other foods...or even your family.

The right way to kill dangerous bacteria on poultry and all other meat is to cook it to a proper internal temperature.

All types of cooked poultry should have an internal temperature of 165 degrees, regardless of whether you use an oven, skillet, or outdoor grill. This cooks the meat all the way through, especially around any bones that may be harboring bacteria.

You can check the temperature by using an oven thermometer—but do notleave the thermometer in the meat while cooking.

Metal thermometers conduct heat and make the area around the thermometer cook faster—throwing off the temperature measurement for the entire piece of meat. (And it will also ruin your thermometer!) Instead, use a thermometer only to sample the temperature when you think the meat is done.

Combination meat dishes, such as lasagna, casseroles, and reheated leftovers, should also reach 165 degrees for at least 15 seconds. Ground meats should hit 155 degrees. And eggs (fried, poached, or scrambled), pork, lamb, seafood, and steaks should cook to 145 degrees.

And the good news for rare-meat lovers is that this temperature still allows for plenty of pink in a juicy steak.

Give yourself a (clean) hand

Of course, you should always wash your hands when preparing food. In fact, improper food handling causes most cases of foodborne illness. Fortunately, there are simple steps you can take to protect you and your family.

Before you start preparing a meal, make sure to remove all accessories, including bracelets, rings, and wristwatches. (This is one case where you don't want to take a licking and keep on ticking). And avoid artificial fingernails (which are unhealthy for nails anyway, especially in people with metabolic and pituitary conditions, as well as diabetes).

All of these accessories can harbor germs, which can contaminate food you touch. (Not that the analogy is appetizing, but as a pathologist who handled human tissue, I never wore jewelry because I got tired of taking it on and off and potentially misplacing or losing it).

Make sure to wash your hands properly and frequently while handling food, and especially after touching raw produce, meat, poultry, or seafood. You need to rub soap on your hands for at least 15 seconds to kill germs.

And avoid antibacterial soaps, which can lead to development and survival of dangerous, resistant strains of bacteria. My daughter's middle school science project demonstrated that simple concept 20 years ago—not to mention all the science that has come out since. But many food safety "experts" still miss this fundamental point.

"Cleaning" kitchen tools isn't the same as sanitizing them

Another thing to watch out for when preparing foods is cross-contamination.

For instance, cutting boards are great for preparing, presenting, and serving foods. But be careful not to use a cutting board to slice raw meat...and then chop vegetables. Even if you wash the board in between, that still may not eliminate all germs left over from the meat.

That's because there is a difference between cleaning and sanitizing. Cleaning removes the visible debris, but sanitizing removes or kills germs at the microscopic level.

To sanitize a cutting board, use hot soap and water, and then wipe with a little bleach solution in water. Or better yet, keep separate cutting boards for meats and for vegetables.

It also matters what type of cutting board you choose. Studies show that wood cutting boards are safer than plastic ones. That's because bacteria can be caught in knife grooves in plastic, and are impossible to clean out. On the other hand, the natural pores in wood are thought to trap and immobilize the bacteria, which eventually and naturally kills it.

When you are done preparing your food, put any ceramic, metal, or plastic utensils in the dishwasher to sanitize them. You can also run sponges through the dishwasher as long as you use a high-heat setting.

Of course, you'll damage wood cutting boards, bowls, or utensils in the dishwasher, so hand wash and sanitize them as I recommended above. And wooden bowls that contain only vegetables or fruit can be wiped clean and "seasoned" with some salt and olive oil to keep them safe.

Store your food properly

Just as heating certain foods is important to kill bacteria, so is keeping them cool.

The FDA recommends you keep your refrigerator at or below 40 degrees Fahrenheit. Most average refrigerator settings are between 35 and 40 degrees, so you should be fine. But if you're concerned, test the temperature with a thermometer. And while you're at it, test the freezer to make sure it's at zero degrees Fahrenheit.

Here's another handy thermostat tip: If you don't keep a fully stocked refrigerator or freezer, or are going to be away for a while, fill the empty spaces with plastic jugs of water. The higher specific heat of water will help your fridge or freezer stay at a constant cold temperature—without using extra energy.

If you want to save leftovers, put them in the refrigerator or freezer within three to four hours after cooking. But don't just place hot food directly in the fridge. Not only does that waste energy, but it may play havoc with the thermostat.

Instead, any cooked food should be allowed to cool to room temperature (this takes about two hours), and then placed in the refrigerator or freezer.

Can't wait for your leftovers to cool? Place the cooking pot in a sink of cold or ice water until the contents get to room temperature.

If you want to freeze your leftovers, put them in smaller, sealable containers labeled with the contents and date. That's important because frozen foods are best consumed within six months.

When it comes time to thaw your food, transfer it from the freezer to the refrigerator a day in advance. But if you are in a hurry, place the frozen food under running warm water, or in a bath of hot water in the sink. Once thawed, eat the food within three days.

Trust your nose and your eyes

Finally, remember to always use a healthy dose of common sense, which eliminates most of the cases of foodborne illness in the home.

That includes using common sense when it comes to "use by" dates stamped on dairy, bread, or other foods you need to buy in packages.

Of course, you should select the packages with the later dates at the store. But don't automatically throw out these foods as soon as they hit the "use-by" date, especially if the package has never been opened. Instead, use your eyes and nose to detect any spoilage.

After all, we have millions of years of biologic adaptation to back us up. If it looks and smells good, it is likely still good to eat.

Know the warning signs of foodborne illness

If you experience the following symptoms, you may have eaten contaminated food. Check with a doctor immediately—especially if you're over age 65 or have a compromised immune system. Both factors can make you more susceptible to developing life-threatening complications from a foodborne illness.

- E. coli infection. Common symptoms include diarrhea, which can range from mild to severe; abdominal cramping; nausea; and vomiting. In severe cases, kidney failure may develop. Most symptoms show up within four days of eating contaminated meat, dairy, or produce.

- Salmonella infection. Often, there are no symptoms. But some people develop diarrhea, abdominal cramps, and fever within eight to 72 hours after eating contaminated food. In rare cases, salmonella can cause acute dehydration or serious diseases like meningitis or infections of the heart (endocarditis) or bones (osteomyelitis).

- Listeriosis. The main symptoms are fever, chills, and severe headaches. Advanced cases may lead to life-threatening septic shock, meningitis, or encephalitis. And beware—although most symptoms appear within a couple days of eating contaminated vegetables or fruits, you can develop listeriosis as long as two months later.

SOURCES

Part 1: Cancer Answers from a True Insider

http://www.angio.org

Cavallo T, Sade R, Folkman J, Cotran RS (1972) Tumor angiogenesis: Rapid induction of endothelial mitoses demonstrated by autoradiography. J Cell Biol 54:408–420

Folkman J, Klagsbrun M (1987) Angiogenic factors. Science 235:442–447

Ausprunk DH, Falterman K, Folkman J (1978) The sequence of events in the regression of corneal capillaries. Lab Invest 38:284–294

Nature (impact factor: 36.28). 01/2006; 438(7070):932-6. DOI:10.1038/nature04478

http://www.angio.org/understanding/fact.php

http://www.scienceofcancers.org/brain-cancer-clinical-trials.php

"Vitamin C and Cancer," in Nutrition and Cancer Prevention: Investigating the Role of Micronutrients. New York: Marcel Dekker, 1989

"How Vitamin C Stops Cancer." ScienceDaily, 9/10/07. (Retrieved 5/29/12, from http://www.sciencedaily.com/releases/2007/09/070910132848.htm)

"Effect of vitamin C on prostate cancer cells in vitro: Effect on cell number, viability, and DNA synthesis," The Prostate 1997; 32(3): 188-195

Cancer Epidemiol Biomarkers Prev 1992; 1: 119

"Can dietary beta-carotene materially reduce human cancer?" Nature 1981; 290: 201-208

"Carotenoid analyses of foods associated with a lower risk for cancer," Journal of the National Cancer Institute 1990; 82: 285-292.

Omenn, G. S. (1998). "Chemoprevention of lung cancer: The rise and demise of beta-carotene," Annual Review of Public Health 1998; 19: 73–99

"Vitamins for Chronic Disease Prevention: Scientific Review and Clinical Applications." Journal of the American Medical Association 2002; 287(23): 3,116-3,129.

"Phase I clinical trial to evaluate the safety, tolerability, and pharmacokinetics of high-dose intravenous ascorbic acid in patients with advanced cancer." Cancer Chemother Pharmacol. 2013; 72(1): 139-146

"Phase I Evaluation of Intravenous Ascorbic Acid in Combination with Gemcitabine and Erlotinib in Patients with Metastatic Pancreatic Cancer," PloS One 2012; 7(1): e29794

"Anti-angiogenic effect of high doses of ascorbic acid," J Transl Med. 2008; 6: 50

Complementary and Integrative Medicine in Cancer Care and Prevention. New York: Springer, 2007, pg. 188-193

www.californiaavocado.com

Aggarwal BB, Bhardwaj A, Aggarwal RS, Seeram NP, Shishodia S, Takada Y. Role of resveratrol in prevention and therapy of cancer: preclinical and clinical studies. Anticancer Res. 2004 Sep-Oct;24(5A):2783-840. http://www.ncbi.nlm.nih.gov/pubmed/15517885?dopt=Abstract

E. Brakenhielm, R. Cao, Y. Cao. FASEB J., 15, 1798–1800 (2001).

K. Igura, T. Ohta, Y. Kuroda, K. Kaji. Cancer Lett., 171, 11–16 (2001).

In Vivo. 2007 Mar-Apr;21(2):365-70

Journal of Experimental & Clinical Cancer Research 2009; 28:124

Drug News Perspect 2009; 22(5): 247-254

Molecular Cancer 2011, 10:12

Bhat TA, Nambiar D, Pal A, Agarwal R, Singh RP. Fisetin inhibits various attributes of angiogenesis in vitro and in vivo—implications for angioprevention. Carcinogenesis. 2012 Feb;33(2):385-93. doi: 10.1093/carcin/bgr282. Epub 2011 Dec 1

"Piperine inhibits PMA-induced cyclooxygenase-2 expression through downregulating NF-kB, C/EBP and AP-1 signaling pathways in murine macrophages," Food Chem Toxicol 2012; 50(7): 2,342-2,348

"Piperine inhibits cytokine production by human peripheral blood mononuclear cells," Genet Mol Res. 2012; 11(1): 617-627

"Piperine suppresses tumor growth and metastasis in vitro and in vivo in a 4T1 murine breast cancer model," Acta Pharmacol Sin 2012; 33(4): 523-530

Crowley 1994:92; Lebot, Merlin and Lindstrom 1992:51-3

Henderson B.E., Kolonel L.N., Dworshy R., Kerford D., Mori E., Sing K and Thevenot H. Cancer incidence in the islands of the Pacific. Nat. Cancer Inst. Monogr. 1985;69:3-81.

Le Marchand L., Hankin J., Bach F., Kolonel L., Wilkens L., Stacewicz- Sapuntzakis M., Bowen P., Beecher G., Laudon F., Baque P., Daniel R., Seruvatu L., Henderson B. An ecological study of diet and lung cancer in the South Pacific. Int. J. Cancer 1995;63:18-23.

Thevenot H., Germain R., Chaubet M. Cancer occurrences in developing countries. IARC Scientific Publication No. 75, Lyon, International Agency for Research on Cancer, 1986;323-329.

http://www.steinerlabs.com/publications/alpha-pyrone-research-on-cancer-incidence/

Castleman, Michael. "Kava Safety Update." Mother Earth Living; January, 2008

http://news.uci.edu/features/can-kava-cure-cancer

Mol Cancer. 2013; 12: 55. Published online 2013 Jun 10.

Nutrition and cancer 06/2012; 64(6):838-46. DOI PubMed

Kava Blocks 4-(Methylnitrosamino)-1-(3-pyridyl)-1-Butanone–Induced Lung Tumorigenesis in Association with Reducing O6-methylguanine DNA Adduct in A/J Mice. Cancer Prevention Research; January, 2014

"Chemotherapy-induced neurotoxicity: the value of neuroprotective strategies." Neth J Med. 2012; 70(1): 18-25

"Metabolic approach to the enhancement of antitumor effect of chemotherapy: a key role of acetyl-L-carnitine," Clin Cancer Res 2010; 16(15): 3,944-3,953

"Induction of ER Stress-Mediated Apoptosis by a-Lipoic Acid in A549 Cell Lines," Korean J Thorac Cardiovasc Surg 2012; 45(1): 1-10

"Lipoic acid - biological activity and therapeutic potential," Pharmacol Rep 2011; 63(4): 849-858

"Coenzyme Q10 for Prevention of Anthracycline-Induced Cardiotoxicity," Integr Cancer Ther 2005; 4(2): 110-130

"Improved survival in patients with end-stage cancer treated with coenzyme Q(10) and other antioxidants: a pilot study," J Int Med Res 2009; 37(6): 1,961-1,971

"Vitamin C and Cancer," in Nutrition and Cancer Prevention: Investigating the Role of Micronutrients. New York: Marcel Dekker, 1989

Complementary and Integrative Medicine in Cancer Care and Prevention. New York: Springer, 2007, pg. 178-186

"Ascorbic acid and cancer: A review," Cancer Research 1979; 39: 663

"A Prospective Study on Folate, B12, and Pyridoxal 5'-Phosphate (B6) and Breast Cancer,"Cancer Epidemiology Biomarkers & Prevention 1999; 8(3): 209–217

"Multivitamin Use, Folate, and Colon Cancer in Women in the Nurses' Health Study,"Annals of Internal Medicine 1998; 129(7): 517-524

Complementary and Integrative Medicine in Cancer Care and Prevention. New York: Springer, 2007, pg. 187-188

"Calcium Supplements for the Prevention of Colorectal Adenomas," New England Journal of Medicine 1999; 340: 101–107

Complementary and Integrative Medicine in Cancer Care and Prevention. New York: Springer, 2007, pg. 269-270

Mian L, et al. Review: The Impacts of Circulating 25-Hydroxyvitamin D Levels on Cancer Patient Outcomes: A Systematic Review and Meta-Analysis. DOI: http://dx.doi.org/10.1210/jc.2013-4320

"Curcumin and its analogues: Potential anticancer agents," Medicinal Research Reviews 2009; 30(5): 818-860 "Curcumin inhibits the migration and invasion of human A549 lung cancer cells through the inhibition of matrix metalloproteinase-2 and-9 and Vascular Endothelial Growth Factor (VEGF)," Cancer Letters 2009; 285(2): 127-133

"Effects of curcumin on bladder cancer cells and development of urothelial tumors in a rat bladder carcinogenesis model," Cancer Lett 2008; 264(2): 299-308

"Effect of curcumin on lung resistance-related protein (LRP) in retinoblastoma cells," Curr Eye Res 2009; 34(10): 845-851

"Allicin inhibits cell growth and induces apoptosis in U87MG human glioblastoma cells through an ERK-dependent pathway," Oncol Rep. 2012; 28(1): 41-48

"Allium vegetables and risk of prostate cancer: a population-based study," J Natl Cancer Inst 2002; 94(21): 1,648-1,651

"Inhibition of the Growth of Human Pancreatic Cancer Cells by the Arginine Antimetabolite L-Canavanine," Cancer Res 1994; 54(23); 6,045-6,048

"GABA's control of stem and cancer cell proliferation in adult neural and peripheral niches," Physiology 2009; 24: 171-185

"African herbal medicines in the treatment of HIV: Hypoxis and Sutherlandia. An overview of evidence and pharmacology," Nutrition Journal 2005; 4: 19

"Medicinal plant 'fights' AIDS," BBC News, 11/30/01. (Retrieved 6/1/12, from http://news.bbc.co.uk/2/hi/africa/1683259. stm)

"Anthropological study of health beliefs, behaviors and outcomes. Traditional folk medicine and ethnopharmacology." Human Organization 1983; 42(4): 351-353

"Chrysanthemum indicum L. Extract Induces Apoptosis through Suppression of Constitutive STAT3 Activation in Human Prostate Cancer DU145 Cells," Phytother Res. 2012 (published online Mar 22)

"Anti-inflammatory effects of the Nigella sativa seed extract, thymoquinone, in pancreatic cancer cells," HPB 2009; 11(5): 373-381

Vitamin D deficiency and mortality risk in the general population: a meta-analysis of prospective cohort studies. Am J Clin Nutr. 2013(97):782-793

American Cancer Society. What are the key statistics about cervical cancer? http://www.cancer.org/cancer/ cervicalcancer/detailedguide/cervical-cancer-key-statistics. Updated April 11, 2013. Accessed October 16, 2013

JAMA Intern Med. 2013;():1-9. doi:10.1001/jamainternmed.2013.2912

Doyle, K. (2013, February 27). Screnning might avert many lung cancer deaths: Study. Retrieved 2013, from http:// www.reuters.com/article/2013/02/27/us-lung-cancer-idUSBRE91Q16F20130227

Rosenthal, Elisabeth. "Let's (not) get physicals," The New York Times, Sunday Review, June 2, 2012.

"Treating you better for less," The New York Times, Sunday Review, June 3, 2012, pg. 12.

"Quantifying the Benefits and Harms of Screening Mammography," JAMA Intern Med (http://archinte.jamanetwork. com/article.aspx?articleid=1792915), December 30, 2013

"Rethinking Screening for Breast Cancer and Prostate Cancer," JAMA 2009;302(15):1685-1692

Institute of Medicine (US) and National Research Council (US) Committee on New Approaches to Early Detection and Diagnosis of Breast Cancer; Joy JE, Penhoet EE, Petitti DB, editors. Saving Women's Lives: Strategies for Improving Breast Cancer Detection and Diagnosis. Washington (DC): National Academies Press (US); 2005.8. "Saving Women's Lives: Strategies for Improving Breast Cancer Detection and Diagnosis," National Institutes of Health (www.ncbi.nlm. nih.gov) 2005

"Cancer? Not!" Medscape (www.medscape.com); Aug 29, 2013

"The $2.7 trillion medical bill: Colonoscopies explain why the U.S. leads the world in health expenditures," The New York Times (www.nytimes.com), 6/1/13

"Can colorectal cancer be prevented?" The American Cancer Society (www.cancer.org), accessed 8/2/13

"Comparative Effectiveness and Cost-effectiveness of Screening Colonoscopy vs. Sigmoidoscopy and Alternative Strategies," Am J Gastroent 2013 108(1):120-132 (http://www.medscape.com/viewarticle/779647_4)

"Less is More: Not 'Going the Distance' and Why," JNCI 2011; 103(23): 1,726-1,728 (http://jnci.oxfordjournals.org/ content/early/2011/11/09/jnci.djr446.full)

"The $2.7 trillion medical bill: Colonoscopies explain why the U.S. leads the world in health expenditures," The New York Times (www.nytimes.com), 6/1/13

"Study: Colonoscopies often come with costly, unnecessary sedation," CBS News (www.cbsnews.com), 3/20/12

Utilization of Anesthesia Services During Outpatient Endoscopies and Colonoscopies and Associated Spending in 2003-2009," JAMA 2012; 307(11): 1,178-1,184 (http://jama.jamanetwork.com/article.aspx?articleid=1105089)

"Reducing Mortality from Colorectal Cancer by Screening for Fecal Occult Blood," NEJM 1993; 328:1365-1371

"Colorectal-Cancer Incidence and Mortality with Screening Flexible Sigmoidoscopy," NEJM 2012; 366:2345-2357

"Once-only flexible sigmoidoscopy screening in prevention of colorectal cancer: a multicentre randomised controlled trial." Lancet 2010;375:1624-1633

"Once-Only Sigmoidoscopy in Colorectal Cancer Screening: Follow-up Findings of the Italian Randomized Controlled Trial—SCORE," JNCI 2011; 103(17):1310-1322

"Thyroid cancer: zealous imaging has increased detection and treatment of low risk tumours." BMJ 2013;347:f4706.

"Low-Risk Thyroid Cancer Overdiagnosed, Overtreated." Available at: http://www.medscape.com/viewarticle/810129. Accessed February 17, 2014

What are the key statistics about breast cancer? (2014, September 9). Retrieved 2014, from http://www.cancer.org/cancer/breastcancer/detailedguide/breast-cancer-key-statistics

"Rethinking the Standard for Ductal Carcinoma In Situ Treatment." *JAMA Oncol.* 2015;1(7):881-883.

"Specific serum carotenoids are inversely associated with breast cancer risk among Chinese women: a case–control study." Br J Nutr. 2015 Oct 20:1-9.

"Meta-analysis of vitamin D sufficiency for improving survival of patients with breast cancer." Anticancer Res. 2014 Mar;34(3):1163-6.

"Effects of selenium supplements on cancer prevention: meta-analysis of randomized controlled trials." Nutr Cancer. 2011 Nov;63(8):1185-95.

Lung Cancer Facts. (n.d.). Retrieved 2014, from https://www.lungcancerfoundation.org/about-us/lung-cancer-facts/

"Vitamin D and lung cancer risk: a comprehensive review and meta-analysis."Cell Physiol Biochem. 2015;36(1):299-305.

"Cloud cover-adjusted ultraviolet B irradiance and pancreatic cancer incidence in 172 countries." J Steroid Biochem Mol Biol. 2015 Apr 9.

"Vitamin D status and surgical outcomes: a systematic review." *Patient Safety in Surgery* 2015, **9**:14.

"Changing Incidence of Serum 25-Hydroxyvitamin D Values Above 50 ng/mL: A 10-Year Population-Based Study." Mayo Clin Proc. 2015 May;90(5):577-86.

Henderson BE, et al. Cancer incidence in the islands of the Pacific. Nat. Cancer Inst. Monogr. 1985;69:3-81.

Leitzman, P, et al. Kava blocks 4-(methylnitrosamino)-1-(3-pyridyl)-1-butanone-induced lung tumorigenesis in association with reducing O6-methylguanine DNA adduct in A/J mice. Cancer Prev Res (Phila). 2014 Jan;7(1):86-96.

Abu N, et al. In vivo antitumor and antimetastatic effects of flavokawain B in 4T1 breast cancer cell-challenged mice. Drug Des Devel Ther. 2015 Mar 6;9:1401-17.

Liu Z, et al. Kava chalcone, flavokawain A, inhibits urothelial tumorigenesis in the UPII-SV40T transgenic mouse model. Cancer Prev Res (Phila). 2013 Dec;6(12):1365-75.

Ji T, et al. Mol Cancer. Flavokawain B, a kava chalcone, inhibits growth of human osteosarcoma cells through G2/M cell cycle arrest and apoptosis. Mol Cancer. 2013 Jun 10;12:55.

Triolet J, et al. Reduction in colon cancer risk by consumption of kava or kava fractions in carcinogen-treated rats. Nutr Cancer. 2012 Aug;64(6):838-46.

Eskander RN, et al. Flavokawain B, a novel, naturally occurring chalcone, exhibits robust apoptotic effects and induces G2/M arrest of a uterine leiomyosarcoma cell line. J Obstet Gynaecol Res. 2012 Aug;38(8):1086-94.

Li X, et al. Kava components down-regulate expression of AR and AR splice variants and reduce growth in patient-derived prostate cancer xenografts in mice. PLoS One. 2012;7(2):e31213.

The Coca-Cola Company. Product Nutrition. http://productnutrition.thecoca-colacompany.com. Accessed April 17, 2015.

"The Effect of Curcumin on Breast Cancer Cells," J Breast Cancer. 2013 Jun; 16(2): 133–137

"Serum lycopene reduces the risk of stroke in men," *Neurology* 2012; 79(15): 1,540-1,547

"Are organic foods safer or healthier than conventional alternatives?: a systematic review." *Ann Intern Med* 2012; 157(5): 348-366

"The Impact of Organic Farming on Quality of Tomatoes Is Associated to Increased Oxidative Stress during Fruit Development," *PlosONE* 2013; 8(2): e56354

"Lycopene Content Among Organically Produced Tomatoes," *Journal of Vegetable Science* 2006; 12(4): 93-106

Schneider C. & Pozzi A. "Cyclooxygenases and lipoxygenases in cancer." Cancer Metastasis Rev. 2011 Dec; 30(0): 277–294.

Meira LB, et al. "DNA damage induced by chronic inflammation contributes to colon carcinogenesis in mice." J Clin Invest. 2008;118(7): 2516-2525.

Al-Salmani K, et al. "A82: Frankincense as a Potentially Novel Therapeutic Agent in Ovarian Cancer." NCRI Cancer Conference poster session abstract. November 2, 2015.

'We bring gifts of gold, myrrh, and ovarian cancer treatment.' Medical News Today, 12/25/2013. https://www.medicalnewstoday.com/articles/270505.php

O'Toole S & O'Leary J. "Ovarian Cancer Chemoresistance." https://link.springer.com/referenceworkentry/10.1007%2F978-3-642-16483-5_6930

Winking M, et al. "Boswellic Acids Inhibit Glioma Growth: A New Treatment Option?" Journal of Neuro-Oncology. 2000 Jan;46(2): 97–103.

Schneider H. & Weller M. "Boswellic acid activity against glioblastoma stem-like cells." Oncol Lett. 2016 Jun; 11(6): 4187–4192.

Kirste S, et al. "Boswellia serrata acts on cerebral edema in patients irradiated for brain tumors: a prospective, randomized, placebo-controlled, double-blind pilot trial." Cancer. 2011 Aug 15;117(16): 3788-95.

Frank et al. "Frankincense oil derived from Boswellia carteri induces tumor cell specific cytotoxicity." BMC Complement Altern Med. 2009; 9:6.

Suhail MM, et al. "Boswellia sacra essential oil induces tumor cell-specific apoptosis and suppresses tumor aggressiveness in cultured human breast cancer cells." BMC Complement Altern Med. 2011;11: 129.

Gerhardt H, Seifert F, Buvari P, Vogelsang H, Repges R. [Therapy of active Crohn disease with Boswellia serrata extract H 15]. Z Gastroenterol. 2001 Jan; 39(1):11–7. [Article in German.]

Yadav VR, et al. "Boswellic acid inhibits growth and metastasis of human colorectal cancer in orthotopic mouse model by downregulating inflammatory, proliferative, invasive and angiogenic biomarkers." International Journal of Cancer. 2012 May;130(9): 2176–2184.

Part 2: Healing Pain Instead of Treating Pain

Goadsby, P.J., MD, D Sc, & Silberstein, S.D., MD. (2013, January 23). Migraine triggers: Harnessing the messages of clinical practice. Neurology, 80(5), 424-425

"Perceived triggers may not actually provoke migraine. Medscape. Jan. 24, 2013.

Holland, S., Silberstein, S., Freitag, F., Dodick, D., Argoff, C., & Ashman, E. (2012, April 24). Evidence-based guidelines update: NSAIDs and other complementary treatments for episodic migraine prevention in adults: Report of the Quality Standards Subcommittee of the American Academy of Neurology and the American Headache Society. Retrieved 2012, from http://www.ncbi.nlm.nih.gov/pubmed/22529203

Diener, H., Rahifs, VW., & Danesch, U. (2004). The First Placebo-controlled Trial of a Special Butterbur Root Extract for the Prevention of Migraine: Reanalysis of Efficacy Criteria. European Neurology Eur Neurol, 51(2), 89-97. Doi: 10.1159/000076535

The Lancet. "Paracetamol no better than placebo for lower back pain." ScienceDaily. ScienceDaily, 24 July 2014. <www.sciencedaily.com/releases/2014/07/140724094025.htm>

"Food and Drug Administration. Assessment of Safety of Aspirin and Other Nonsteroidal Anti-Inflammatory Drugs (NSAIDs)." Available at: http://www.fda.gov/ohrms/dockets/ac/02/briefing/3882b2_02_mcneil-nsaid.htm. Accessed February 18, 2014

Rabago D, et al. Dextrose Prolotherapy for Knee Osteoarthritis: A Randomized Controlled Trial. Ann Fam Med May/June 2013 vol. 11 no. 3 229-237.

"Drug Resistance and Pseudoresistance: An Unintended Consequence of Enteric Coating Aspirin" Circulation. 2012;CIRCULATIONAHA.112.117283 published online before print December 4 2012, doi:10.1161/CIRCULATIONAHA.112.117283

"Could tarantula venom help fight pain?" Medical News Today (www.medicalnewstoday.com) 2/29/2016

Astone, N.M., Martin, S., & Aron, L.Y. (2015, March 5). Death Rates for US Women Ages 15 to 54. Retrieved 2015, from http://www.urban.org/research/publication/death-rates-us-women-ages-15-54

Rising morbidity and mortality in midlife among white non-Hispanic Americans in the 21st century." Proc Natl Acad Sci U S A. 2015 Dec 8;112(49):15078-83.

"Acceptability of a Guided Imagery Intervention for Persons Undergoing a Total Knee Replacement." Orthop Nurs. 2015 Nov-Dec;34(6):356-64.

"Effectiveness of mindfulness meditation on pain and quality of life of patients with chronic low back pain." Int J Yoga. 2015 Jul-Dec;8(2):128-33.

"Observing the Effects of Mindfulness-Based Meditation on Anxiety and Depression in Chronic Pain Patients." Psychiatr Danub. 2015 Sep;27 Suppl 1:S209-11.

"Management of osteoarthritis (OA) with the pharma-standard supplement FlexiQule (Boswellia): a 12-week registry." Minerva Gastroenterol Dietol. 2015 Oct 22.

"Curcumin loaded solid lipid nanoparticles ameliorate adjuvant-induced arthritis in rats." Eur J Pain. 2015 Aug;19(7):940-52.

"A new curcuma extract (flexofytol®) in osteoarthritis: results from a belgian real-life experience." Open Rheumatol J. 2014 Oct 17;8:77-81.

"Co-analgesic therapy for arthroscopic supraspinatus tendon repair pain using a dietary supplement containing Boswellia serrata and Curcuma longa: a prospective randomized placebo-controlled study." Musculoskelet Surg. 2015 Sep;99 Suppl 1:S43-52.

"Efficacy and Safety of Fish Oil in Treatment of Knee Osteoarthritis." J Med Assoc Thai. 2015 Apr;98 Suppl 3:S110-4.

"Fish oil in knee osteoarthritis: a randomised clinical trial of low dose versus high dose." Ann Rheum Dis. 2016 Jan;75(1):23-9."An aerobic walking programme versus muscle strengthening programme for chronic low back pain: a randomized controlled trial," *Clinical Rehabilitation*2013; 27(3): 207-214

"Repetitive Transcranial Magnetic Stimulation Once a Week Induces Sustainable Long-Term Relief of Central Poststroke Pain," Neuromodulation: Technology at the Neural Interface June 2015; 18(4): 249–254

Part 3: Brain-Healers from Behind the Curtain

"Higher normal fasting plasma glucose is associated with hippocampal atrophy: The PATH Study,"Neurology 2012; 79:1,019-1,026

"Impaired insulin and insulin-like growth factor expression and signaling mechanisms in Alzheimer's disease—is this type 3 diabetes?" J Alzheimers Dis 2005; 7(1): 63–80

"Berberine: A potential multipotent natural product to combat Alzheimer's Disease," Molecules 2011; 16: 6,732-6,740

"Oren-gedoku-to and its Constituents with Therapeutic Potential in Alzheimer's Disease Inhibit Indoleamine 2, 3-Dioxygenase Activity In Vitro," J Alzheimers Dis 2010; 22(1):257-66

Molecular Basis of Inhibitory Activities of Berberine against Pathogenic Enzymes in Alzheimer's Disease," The Scientific World Journal vol. 2012, Article ID 823201 (doi:10.1100/2012/823201)

Grimming B, et al. "Neuroprotective mechanisms of astaxanthin: a potential therapeutic role in preserving cognitive function in age and neurodegeneration." GeroScience 2017; 39:19–32

Johnson EJ. "A possible role for lutein and zeaxanthin in cognitive function in the elderly." Am J Clin Nutr 2012;96(suppl):1161S–5S.

"Parahippocampal Cortex Mediates the Relationship between Lutein and Crystallized Intelligence in Healthy, Older Adults." Front Aging Neurosci. 2016 Dec 6;8:297.

Feart C, et al. "Plasma Carotenoids Are Inversely Associated With Dementia Risk in an Elderly French Cohort." J Gerontol A Biol Sci Med Sci. 2016 May;71(5):683-8.

"Astaxanthin May Be Key to Longevity," Newsmax (www.newsmax.com) 10/9/2017

Feeney J, et al. "Plasma Lutein and Zeaxanthin Are Associated With Better Cognitive Function Across Multiple Domains in a Large Population-Based Sample of Older Adults: Findings from The Irish Longitudinal Study on Aging." J Gerontol A Biol Sci Med Sci. 2017 Oct 1;72(10):1431-1436.

"Supplementation with macular carotenoids reduces psychological stress, serum cortisol, and sub-optimal symptoms of physical and emotional health in young adults." Nutr Neurosci. 2017 Feb 15:1-11.

Effect of Vitamin E and Memantine on Functional Decline in Alzheimer Disease – The TEAM-AD VA Cooperative Randomized Trial," JAMA. 2014; 311(1): 33-34

"Current evidence for the use of coffee and caffeine to prevent age-related cognitive decline and Alzheimer's disease," Journal of Nutrition, Health & Aging 2014: 18(4): 383-392

"Self-Reported Increased Confusion or Memory Loss and Associated Functional Difficulties Among Adults Aged ≥60 Years — 21 States, 2011," Centers for Disease Control (www.cdc.com) 5/10/2013

Desideri G, et al. Benefits in cognitive function, blood pressure, and insulin resistance through cocoa flavanol consumption in elderly subjects with mild cognitive impairment: the Cocoa, Cognition, and Aging (CoCoA) study. Hypertension. 2012 Sep;60(3):794-801. doi: 10.1161/HYPERTENSIONAHA.112.193060. Epub 2012 Aug 14.

Brickman AM, et al. Enhancing dentate gyrus function with dietary flavanols improves cognition in older adults. Nat Neurosci. 2014 Dec;17(12):1798-803. doi: 10.1038/nn.3850. Epub 2014 Oct 26.

Harwood ML, et al. Tolerance for high flavanol cocoa powder in semisweet chocolate. *Nutrients*. 2013;5(6):2258-2267.

"Xanthohumol, a Polyphenol Chalcone Present in Hops, Activating Nrf2 Enzymes To Confer Protection against Oxidative Damage in PC12 Cells." J. Agric. Food Chem., 2015, 63 (5), pp 1521–1531

"Finally, a beer that will solve your creative problems," Fast Company (www.fastcocreate.com), 12/18/14

"Flavonoid-rich orange juice is associated with acute improvements in cognitive function in healthy middle-aged males." Eur J Nutr (2016) 55: 2021.

Fox, M, Knapp, LA, Andrews, PW, Fincher, CL, Hygeine and the world distribution of Alzheimer's disease, *Evolution, Medicine and Public Health*, 2013, DOI: 10.1093/emph/eot015.

Ratner, E and Atkinson, D, J Am Geriatr Soc 2015: 63(12): 2612-2614

"Meta-analysis of modifiable risk factors for Alzheimer's disease," J Neurol Neurosurg Psychiatry (www.jnnp.bmj.com) 8/20/2015

"Neurological diseases remain neglected and ignored." *Lancet* 2012; 379: 287

"The road to 25×25: how can the five-target strategy reach its destination?"*Lancet Global Health* 2014; 2:e126.

"Forecasting the global burden of Alzheimer's disease." *Alzheimers Demen*2007; 3: 186–91.

"Neurodegenerative diseases: an overview of environmental risk factors."*Environ Health Perspect* 2005; 113: 1250–6.

"The role of environmental exposures in neurodegeneration and neurodegenerative diseases." *Toxicol Sci* 2011; 124: 225–50.

"Mitochondrial dysfunction in Parkinson's disease: molecular mechanisms and pathophysiological consequences." *EMBO J.* 2012; 31(14): 3038-62.

"Occupational and environmental risk factors for Parkinson's disease."*Parkinsonism Relat Disord* 2002; 8: 297–309.

"What we truly know about occupation as a risk factor for ALS: a critical and systematic review." *Amyotroph Lateral Scler* 2009; 10: 295–U70.

"Severely increased risk of amyotrophic lateral sclerosis among Italian professional football players." Brain 2005; 128: 472–6.

"Preventing Alzheimer's disease-related gray matter atrophy by B-vitamin treatment." *PNAS* 2013; 110(23): 9523–9528

"Vitamin D and the risk of dementia and Alzheimer disease." *Neurology*2014; 83(10):920-8

"New Studies Focus on Vitamin D and MS." National MS Society (www.nationalmssociety.org). Accessed 9/16/14.

"Effect of Vitamin E and Memantine on Functional Decline in Alzheimer Disease – The TEAM-AD VA Cooperative Randomized Trial," *JAMA* 2014; 311(1): 33-34.

"Nicotine from edible *Solanaceae* and risk of Parkinson disease." *Annals of Neurology* 2013; 74(3): 472–477.

"Age at obesity and association with subsequent dementia: record linkage study." *Postgrad Med J* 2014; 90(1,068): 547-51

"The effects of an 8-week hatha yoga intervention on executive function in older adults." *J Gerontol A Biol Sci Med Sci.* 2014; 69(9): 1109-16.

Part 4: Master Your Heart Health

"Blood tests for heart disease." http://www.mayoclinic.org/diseases-conditions/heart-disease/in-depth/heart-disease/art-20049357. Accessed March 24, 2014.

"Moderate elevation of body iron level and increased risk of cancer occurrence and death." Int J Cancer. 1994 Feb 1;56(3):364-9.

Muller H, et al. The Serum LDL/HDL Cholesterol Ratio Is Influenced More Favorably by Exchanging Saturated with Unsaturated Fat Than by Reducing Saturated Fat in the Diet of Women. J. Nutr. January 1, 2003 vol. 133 no. 1 78-83.

Nichols AB, et al. Daily nutritional intake and serum lipid levels. The Tecumseh study.Am J Clin Nutr. 1976 Dec;29(12):1384-92.

Dreon DM, et al. Change in dietary saturated fat intake is correlated with change in mass of large low-density-lipoprotein particles in men. Am J Clin Nutr. May 1998 vol. 67 no. 5 828-836.

Siri-Tarino, PW. Meta-analysis of prospective cohort studies evaluating the association of saturated fat with cardiovascular disease. Am J Clin Nutr. January 2010 ajcn.27725

Lemos da Luz P, et al. High Ratio of Triglycerides to HDL-Cholesterol Predicts Extensive Coronary Disease. Clinics. Aug 2008; 63(4): 427–432

Sachdeva A, et al. Lipid levels in patients hospitalized with coronary artery disease: an analysis of 136,905 hospitalizations in Get With The Guidelines

Weverling-Rijnsburger AWE, et al. Total cholesterol and risk of mortality in the oldest old. The Lancet. Volume 350, Issue 9085, 18 October 1997, Pages 1119–1123

Neaton JD, et al. Serum Cholesterol Level and Mortality Findings for Men Screened in the Multiple Risk Factor Intervention Trial. Arch Intern Med.1992;152(7):1490-1500. doi:10.1001/archinte.1992.00400190110021

Lack of Vitamin D Linked to CVD Biomarkers, Inflammation," Medscape (www.medscape.com) 2/27/2014

"Vitamin D deficiency is associated with inflammation in older Irish adults," J Clin Endocrinol Metab 2014

European Society of Human Genetics (ESHG). "Genetic research clarifies link between hypertension and Vitamin D deficiency." ScienceDaily. www.sciencedaily.com/releases/2013/06/130610192638.htm (accessed March 16, 2018).

"Demographic Differences and Trends of Vitamin D Insufficiency in the US Population, 1988-2004" Arch Intern Med. 2009;169(6):626-632

"Total Joint Arthroplasty and the Risk of Myocardial Infarction: A General Population, Propensity Score-Matched Cohort Study." Arthritis Rheumatol. 2015 Oct;67(10):2771-9.

"Plasma total homocysteine, B vitamins, and risk of coronary atherosclerosis."Arterioscler Thromb Vasc Biol. 1997 May;17(5):989-95.

"The kidney and homocysteine metabolism." J Am Soc Nephrol. 2001 Oct;12(10):2181-9.

"Metformin activates an atypical PKC-CBP pathway to promote neurogenesis and enhance spatial memory formation." Cell Stem Cell, volume 11, issue 1, 23-25, 6 July 2012.

The New York Times. Declining Lethality.http://www.nytimes.com/interactive/2014/01/05/sunday-review/declining-lethality.html?_r=0. Accessed January 24, 2015.

Ingenbleek Y, McCully KS. Vegetarianism produces subclinical malnutrition, hyperhomocysteinemia and atherogenesis. Nutrition. 2012 Feb;28(2):148-53. doi: 10.1016/j.nut.2011.04.009. Epub 2011 Aug 27.

Selhub J, et al. Vitamin status and intake as primary determinants of homocysteinemia in an elderly population. JAMA 1993;270:2693–8.

Saposnik G, et al. Homocysteine-lowering therapy and stroke risk, severity, and disability: additional findings from the HOPE 2 trial. Stroke. 2009 Apr;40(4):1365-72. doi: 10.1161/STROKEAHA.108.529503. Epub 2009 Feb 19.

Spence JD, et al. Vitamin Intervention For Stroke Prevention trial: an efficacy analysis. Stroke. 2005 Nov;36(11):2404-9. Epub 2005 Oct 20.

"Factors associated with no apparent coronary artery disease in patients with type 2 diabetes mellitus for more than 10 years of duration: a case control study," Cardiovasc Diabetol 2015; 14(146)

Henry, J.P. and Micozzi, M.S. (1977) Influence of psychosocial stimulation and early experience on blood pressure in infancy and childhood, Medical College Pennsylvania, Ciba Symposium on Hypertension in Children, Adolescents and Young Adults, Philadelphia, Pennsylvania.

Micozzi, M.S. (1980) Childhood hypertension and academic standing in the Philippines, American Journal of Public Health 70: 530-532.

James PA, et al. 2014 Evidence-Based Guideline for the Management of High Blood Pressure in Adults. Report From the Panel Members Appointed to the Eighth Joint National Committee (JNC 8). JAMA. 2014;311(5):507-520. doi: 10.1001/jama. 2013.284427.

Rodriguez C, et al. Waste and Harm in the Treatment of Hypertension. Journal of the American Medical Association Internal Medicine June 10, 2013; 173(11): 956-957.

Sim JJ, et al. Impact of Achieved Blood Pressures on Mortality Risk and End-Stage Renal Disease Among a Large, Diverse Hypertension Population. J Am Coll Cardiol 2014; 64(6), 588-597.

Risky Drugs: Why the FDA Cannot be Trusted. http://www.bibliotecapleyades.net/ciencia/ciencia_industryweapons295.htm. Accessed August 21, 2014.

Alzheimer's Association International Conference (AAIC) 2014. Abstract P2-083. Presented July 14, 2014.

Gottesman RF, et al. Midlife Hypertension and 20-Year Cognitive Change: The Atherosclerosis Risk in Communities Neurocognitive Study. JAMA Neurol. 2014 Aug 4. doi: 10.1001/jamaneurol.2014.1646.

"Conjugated linoleic acid in adipose tissue and risk of myocardial infarction," Am. J Clin Nutr 2010 Jul;92(1):34-40

"Cellular and molecular mechanisms of statins: an update on pleiotropic effects." Clin Sci (Lond). 2015 Jul 1;129(2):93-105.

Howard BV, et al. Low-fat dietary pattern and weight change over 7 years: the Women's Health Initiative Dietary Modification Trial. JAMA. 2006; 295:39-49.

Brinton EA, et al. A low-fat diet decreases high density lipoprotein (HDL) cholesterol levels by decreasing HDL apolipoprotein transport rates. J Clin Invest. Jan 1990; 85(1): 144–151.

Dreon DM, et al. Reduced LDL particle size in children consuming a very-low-fat diet is related to parental LDL-subclass patterns. Am J Clin Nutr. June 2000 vol. 71 no. 6 1611-1616.

"Processed foods: contributions to nutrition," Am J Clin Nutr 2014; Apr 23 (epub ahead of print)

Muller H, et al. The Serum LDL/HDL Cholesterol Ratio Is Influenced More Favorably by Exchanging Saturated with Unsaturated Fat Than by Reducing Saturated Fat in the Diet of Women. J. Nutr. January 1, 2003 vol. 133 no. 1 78-83.

Nichols AB, et al. Daily nutritional intake and serum lipid levels. The Tecumseh study.Am J Clin Nutr. 1976 Dec;29(12):1384-92.

Dreon DM, et al. Change in dietary saturated fat intake is correlated with change in mass of large low-density-lipoprotein particles in men.Am J Clin Nutr. May 1998 vol. 67 no. 5 828-836.

Siri-Tarino, PW. Meta-analysis of prospective cohort studies evaluating the association of saturated fat with cardiovascular disease. Am J Clin Nutr. January 2010 ajcn.27725.

American Heart Association. Trans Fats.http://www.heart.org/HEARTORG/GettingHealthy/FatsAndOils/Fats101/Trans-Fats_UCM_301120_Article.jsp. Accessed April 16, 2014.Lemos da Luz P, et al. High Ratio of Triglycerides to HDL-Cholesterol Predicts Extensive Coronary Disease. Clinics. Aug 2008; 63(4): 427–432.

Sachdeva A, et al. Lipid levels in patients hospitalized with coronary artery disease: an analysis of 136,905 hospitalizations in Get With The Guidelines.

Am Heart J. 2009 Jan;157(1):111-117.e2. doi: 10.1016/j.ahj.2008.08.010.

Weverling-Rijnsburger AWE, et al. Total cholesterol and risk of mortality in the oldest old. The Lancet. Volume 350, Issue 9085, 18 October 1997, Pages 1119–1123.

Neaton JD, et al. Serum Cholesterol Level and Mortality Findings for Men Screened in the Multiple Risk Factor Intervention Trial. Arch Intern Med.1992;152(7):1490-1500. doi:10.1001/archinte.1992.00400190110021.

Gillman MW, et al. Margarine intake and subsequent coronary heart disease in men. Epidemiology. 1997 Mar;8(2):144-9.

Ramsden CE, et al. Use of dietary linoleic acid for secondary prevention of coronary heart disease and death: evaluation of recovered data from the Sydney Diet Heart Study and updated meta-analysis BMJ 2013;346:e8707

USDA. Adoption of Genetically Engineered Crops in the U.S. http://www.ers.usda.gov/data-products/adoption-of-genetically-engineered-crops-in-the-us/recent-trends-in-ge-adoption.aspx#.U07t4sbjPgI. Accessed April 16, 2014.

Russo, GL. Dietary n-6 and n-3 polyunsaturated fatty acids: from biochemistry to clinical implications in cardiovascular prevention. Biochem Pharmacol. 2009 Mar 15;77(6):937-46. doi: 10.1016/j.bcp.2008.10.020. Epub 2008 Oct 28.

O'Keefe, S, et al. Levels of trans geometrical isomers of essential fatty acids in some unhydrogenated U.S. vegetable oils. Journal of Food Lipids.Volume 1, Issue 3, pages 165–176, September 1994.

"Potent anti-obese principle from Rosa canina: structural requirements and mode of action of trans-tiliroside." Bioorg Med Chem Lett. 2007;17:3059–3064.

"Rosehip extract inhibits lipid accumulation in white adipose tissue by suppressing the expression of peroxisome proliferator-activated receptor gamma." Prev Nutr Food Sci. 2013;18:85–91.

"Effects of rose hip intake on risk markers of type 2 diabetes and cardiovascular disease: a randomized, double-blind, cross-over investigation in obese persons." Eur J Clin Nutr. 2012;66:585–590.

"Daily intake of rosehip extract decreases abdominal visceral fat in preobese subjects: a randomized, double-blind, placebo-controlled clinical trial." Diabetes Metab Syndr Obes. 2015; 8: 147–156.

"Is Organic Agriculture 'Affluent Narcissism'?" Forbes (www.forbes.com) 11/7/2012

"Distinguishable Epidemics of Multidrug Resistant Salmonella Typhimurium DT104 In Different Hosts," Science 9/27/2013; 341(6153):1514-1517

"Organic foods vs. supermarket foods: Element levels," Journal of Applied Nutrition 1993; 45:35-39

"New Evidence Settles a Lingering Question – Is Organic Food More Nutritious?," Organic Consumers Association (www.organicconsumers.org) 3/19/2008

"Natural Sunscreen Agents: A Review," Sch. Acad. J. Pharm., 2013; 2(6):458-463

"Comparison of antioxidant potency of commonly consumed polyphenol-rich beverages in the United States." J Agric Food Chem. 2008 Feb 27;56(4):1415-22.

Daley, C. A., Abbott, A., Doyle, P.S., Nader, G. A., & Larson, S. (2010). A review of fatty acid profiles and antioxidant content in grass-fed and grain-fed beef. *Nutrition Journal Nutr J,* 9(1). doi:10.1186/1475-2891-9-10

EWG's Shopper's Guide to Pesticides in Produce. (n.d). Retrieved 9/1/2015, from http://www.ewg.org/foodnews/dirty_dozen_list.php

EWG's Shopper's Guide to Pesticides in Produce. (n.d). Retrieved 9/1/2015, from https://www.ewg.org/foodnews/clean_fifeteen_list.php

Food Storage Chart for Cupboard/Pantry, Refrigerator and Freezer. (n.d). Retrieved 9/1/2015, from http://food.unl.edu/food-storage-chart-cupboardpantry-refridgerator-and-freezer

Food Waste: The Facts. (n.d.). Retrieved 9/1/15, from http://www.worldfooddayusa.ord/food_waste_the_facts

Pendick, D. (2015, March 05). Peanuts linked to same heart, longevity benefits as more pricey nuts – Harvard Health Blog. Retrieved 9/1/2016, from http://www.health.harvard.edu/blog/peanuts-linked-heart-longevity-benefits-pricey-nuts-201503057777

"The Association between Insomnia Symptoms and Mortality: A Prospective Study of U.S. Men," Circulation 2013;

"Continuous Positive Airway Pressure Treatment of Mild to Moderate Obstructive Sleep Apnea Reduces Cardiovascular Risk," American Journal of Respiratory and Critical Care Medicine 2007; 176(12): 1274-1280.

Part 5: Conquering Everyday Health

"Vitamin D and gastrointestinal diseases: inflammatory bowel disease and colorectal cancer," Therap Adv Gastroenterol. 2011 January; 4(1): 49–62

"Plasma 25-hydroxyvitamin D and colorectal cancer risk according to tumour immunity status," Gut; published online 1/15/2015

Vitamin D status and survival of metastatic colorectal cancer patients: Results from CALGB/SWOG 80405," J Clin Oncol 2015; 33

"The phytoestrogen prunetin affects body composition and improves fitness and lifespan in male *Drosophila melanogaster.*" *The FASEB Journal* 2016; 30(2): 948-958

"Individual variability in human blood metabolites identifies age-related differences." Proceedings of the National Academy of Sciences, 2016; 113(16):4252-9

"Effects of blueberry supplementation on measures of functional mobility in older adults." Appl Physiol Nutr Metab. 2015 Jun;40(6):543-9.

"Effects of Lifestyle Modification on Telomerase Gene Expression in Hypertensive Patients: A Pilot Trial of Stress Reduction and Health Education Programs in African Americans." PLoS One. 2015 Nov 16;10(11):e0142689.

"Metformin promotes lifespan through mitohormesis via the peroxiredoxin PRDX-2." Proc Natl Acad Sci U S A. 2014 Jun 17;111(24):E2501-9.

"Metformin improves health span and lifespan in mice." Nat Commun.2013;4:2192.

Life Extension. (2015, December 16). Anti-aging human study on metformin wins FDA approval. Retrieved 2015, frim http://www.prnewswire.com/news-releases/anti-aging-human-study-on-metformin-wins-fda-approval-300193724.html

"A nutrigenomics approach for the study of anti-aging interventions: olive oil phenols and the modulation of gene and microRNA expression profiles in mouse brain." Eur J Nutr. 2015 Dec 22.

"Brain atrophy in cognitively impaired elderly: the importance of long-chain ω-3 fatty acids and B vitamin status in a randomized controlled trial." Am J Clin Nutr July 2015 vol. 102 no. 1 215-221.

Hearing Loss Association of America. Basic Facts About Hearing Loss.http://www.hearingloss.org/content/basic-facts-about-hearing-loss. Accessed January 26, 2015.

Bush AL, et al. Peripheral Hearing and Cognition: Evidence From the Staying Keen in Later Life (SKILL) Study. Ear Hear. 2015 Jan 13.

Chen DS, et al. Association of Hearing Impairment with Declines in Physical Functioning and the Risk of Disability in Older Adults. J Gerontol A Biol Sci Med Sci. 2014 Dec 3. pii: glu207.

Choi YH, et al. Antioxidant vitamins and magnesium and the risk of hearing loss in the US general population. Am J Clin Nutr. 2014 Jan;99(1):148-55. doi: 10.3945/ajcn.113.068437.

Brown KD, et al. Activation of SIRT3 by the NAD+ Precursor Nicotinamide Riboside Protects from Noise-Induced Hearing Loss. Cell Metabolism, Volume 20, Issue 6, p1059–1068, 2 December 2014.

Kyle ME, et al. Impact of Nonaspirin Nonsteroidal Anti-inflammatory Agents and Acetaminophen on Sensorineural Hearing Loss: A Systematic Review.

Otolaryngol Head Neck Surg. 2015 Jan 5. pii: 0194599814564533.

"Impact of Statins on Biological Characteristics of Stem Cells Provides a Novel Explanation for Their Pleotropic Beneficial and Adverse Clinical Effects," American Journal of Physiology – Cell Physiology; 7/29/2015

"Vitamin C Is Associated with Reduced Risk of Cataract in a Mediterranean Population," J. Nutr. June 1, 2002; 132(6): 1299-1306

"Prospective Study of Dietary Fat and Risk of Cataract Extraction among US Women," American Journal of Epidemiology December 14, 2004; 161(10): 1-12

"Black and Green Teas Equally Inhibit Diabetic Cataracts in a Streptozotocin-Induced Rat Model of Diabetes," J. Agric. Food Chem., 2005, 53 (9): 3710–3713

"Dietary carbohydrate in relation to cortical and nuclear lens opacities in the melbourne visual impairment project," Invest Ophthalmol Vis Sci. 2010 Jun;51(6): 2897-905

"Green Tea Catechins and Their Oxidative Protection in the Rat Eye," J. Agric. Food Chem., 2010, 58 (3): 1523–1534

Part 6: 9 Secrets to Stop Aging in its Tracks

"The phytoestrogen prunetin affects body composition and improves fitness and lifespan in male *Drosophila melanogaster*." *The FASEB Journal* 2016; 30(2): 948-958

"Individual variability in human blood metabolites identifies age-related differences." Proceedings of the National Academy of Sciences, 2016; 113(16):4252-9

"Effects of blueberry supplementation on measures of functional mobility in older adults." Appl Physiol Nutr Metab. 2015 Jun;40(6):543-9.

"Effects of Lifestyle Modification on Telomerase Gene Expression in Hypertensive Patients: A Pilot Trial of Stress Reduction and Health Education Programs in African Americans." PLoS One. 2015 Nov 16;10(11):e0142689.

"Metformin promotes lifespan through mitohormesis via the peroxiredoxin PRDX-2." Proc Natl Acad Sci U S A. 2014 Jun 17;111(24):E2501-9.

"Metformin improves healthspan and lifespan in mice." Nat Commun.2013;4:2192.

Life Extension. (2015, December 16). Anti-aging human study on metformin wins FDA approval. Retrieved 2015, from http://www.prnewswire.com/news-releases/anti-aging-human-study-on-metformin-wins-fda-approval-300193724.html

"A nutrigenomics approach for the study of anti-aging interventions: olive oil phenols and the modulation of gene and microRNA expression profiles in mouse brain." Eur J Nutr. 2015 Dec 22.

"Brain atrophy in cognitively impaired elderly: the importance of long-chain ω-3 fatty acids and B vitamin status in a randomized controlled trial." Am J Clin Nutr July 2015 vol. 102 no. 1 215-221.

Hearing Loss Association of America. Basic Facts About Hearing 11Loss.http://www.hearingloss.org/content/basic-facts-about-hearing-loss. Accessed January 26, 2015.

Bush AL, et al. Peripheral Hearing and Cognition: Evidence From the Staying Keen in Later Life (SKILL) Study. Ear Hear. 2015 Jan 13.

Chen DS, et al. Association of Hearing Impairment with Declines in Physical Functioning and the Risk of Disability in Older Adults. J Gerontol A Biol Sci Med Sci. 2014 Dec 3. pii: glu207.

Choi YH, et al. Antioxidant vitamins and magnesium and the risk of hearing loss in the US general population. Am J Clin Nutr. 2014 Jan;99(1):148-55. doi: 10.3945/ajcn.113.068437.

Brown KD, et al. Activation of SIRT3 by the NAD+ Precursor Nicotinamide Riboside Protects from Noise-Induced Hearing Loss. Cell Metabolism, Volume 20, Issue 6, p1059–1068, 2 December 2014.

Kyle ME, et al. Impact of Nonaspirin Nonsteroidal Anti-inflammatory Agents and Acetaminophen on Sensorineural Hearing Loss: A Systematic Review. Otolaryngol Head Neck Surg. 2015 Jan 5. pii: 0194599814564533.

"Impact of Statins on Biological Characteristics of Stem Cells Provides a Novel Explanation for Their Pleotropic Beneficial and Adverse Clinical Effects," American Journal of Physiology – Cell Physiology; 7/29/2015

"Vitamin C Is Associated with Reduced Risk of Cataract in a Mediterranean Population," J. Nutr. June 1, 2002; 132(6): 1299-1306

"Prospective Study of Dietary Fat and Risk of Cataract Extraction among US Women," American Journal of Epidemiology December 14, 2004; 161(10): 1-12

"Black and Green Teas Equally Inhibit Diabetic Cataracts in a Streptozotocin-Induced Rat Model of Diabetes," J. Agric. Food Chem., 2005, 53 (9): 3710–3713

"Dietary carbohydrate in relation to cortical and nuclear lens opacities in the melbourne visual impairment project," Invest Ophthalmol Vis Sci. 2010 Jun;51(6): 2897-905

"Green Tea Catechins and Their Oxidative Protection in the Rat Eye," J. Agric. Food Chem., 2010, 58 (3): 1523–1534

Part 7: A Drug-Free Guide to Defeating Your Depression

"Does long term use of psychiatric drugs cause more harm than good?" BMJ 2015;350:h2435.

"Specific SSRIs and birth defects: Bayesian analysis to interpret new data in the context of previous reports." BMJ 2015;351:h3190.

"Risk of intracranial haemorrhage in antidepressant users with concurrent use of non-steroidal anti-inflammatory drugs: nationwide propensity score matched study." BMJ 2015;351:h3517.

"Antidepressant Use Is Associated With an Increased Risk of Developing Microbleeds." Stroke. 2016; 47: 251-254

"p53, a target of estrogen receptor (ER) α, modulates DNA damage-induced growth suppression in ER-positive breast cancer cells." J Biol Chem. 2012 Aug 31;287(36):30117-27.

"AroER tri-screen is a biologically relevant assay for endocrine disrupting chemicals modulating the activity of aromatase and/or the estrogen receptor." Toxicol Sci. 2014 May;139(1):198-209.

"QT interval and antidepressant use: a cross sectional study of electronic health records." BMJ 2013;346:f288.

"Antidepressant-induced liver injury: a review for clinicians." Am J Psychiatry.2014 Apr;171(4):404-15.

"Vitamin D Supplementation for Depressive Symptoms: A Systematic Review and Meta-analysis of Randomized Controlled Trials" Psychosomatic Medicine, April 2014; 76(3): 190-196.

"Effects of vitamin D supplementation on symptoms of depression in overweight and obese subjects: randomized double blind trial. Journal of Internal Medicine, December 2008; 264(6):599-609

"Vitamin D and the omega-3 fatty acids control serotonin synthesis and action, part 2: relevance for ADHD, bipolar disorder, schizophrenia, and impulsive behavior, June 2015; 29(6):2207-22

http://ajcn.nutrition.org/content/92/2/330.abstract

"Treatment of depression: time to consider folic acid and vitamin B12, January 2005; 19(1):59-65

"Omega-3 polyunsaturated fatty acid (PUFA) status in major depressive disorder with comorbid anxiety disorders." Journal of Clinical Psychiatry, July 2013; 74(7):732-8

"Omega-3 fatty acids for depression in adults" Cochrane Database System Review, November 2015

"The impact of whole-of-diet interventions on depression and anxiety: a systematic review of randomised controlled trials," Public Health Nutr. 2014 Dec 3:1-2

Food and the brain. Program and abstracts of the American Psychiatric Association 168th Annual Meeting; May 16-20, 2015; Toronto, Ontario, Canada. Workshop

Mollusks, oyster, eastern, wild, raw Nutrition Facts & Calories. (2014). Retrieved 2014, http://nutritiondata.self.com/facts/finfish-and-shellfish-products/4189/2

"Mediterranean dietary pattern and depression: the PREDIMED randomized trial," BMC Medicine 2013;11: 208

"Discrepancy between the Atwater factor predicted and empirically measured energy values of almonds in human diets." Am J Clin Nutr. 2012 Aug; 96(2): 296-301.

"Vegetarian diet and mental disorders: results from a representative community survey." Int J Behav Nutr Phys Act. 2012 Jun 7; 9: 67.

"Prevalence of celiac disease and gluten sensitivity in the United States clinical antipsychotic trials of intervention effectiveness study population." Schizophr Bull. 2011 Jan; 37(1): 94-100.

"A randomized controlled trial to test the effect of multispecies probiotics on cognitive reactivity to sad mood." Brain Behav Immun. 2015 Aug; 48:258-64.

"Research update: healthy aging and prevention of late-life mood and cognitive disorders." American Association for Geriatric Psychiatry 2015 Annual Meeting, session 303.

Cosgrove, L., Bursztajn, H. J., Erlich, D. R., Wheeler, E. E. and Shaughnessy, A. F. (2012), Conflicts of interest and the quality of recommendations in clinical guidelines. *Journal of Evaluation in Clinical Practice*. doi: 10.1111/jep.12016

Presented at the American Academy of Neurology's 65th Annual Meeting in San Diego, March 16 to 23, 2013

"Vitamin D and the omega-3 fatty acids control serotonin synthesis and action, part 2: relevance for ADHD, bipolar, schizophrenia, and impulsive behavior," FASEB journal (Federation of American Societies for Experimental Biology), Published online before print February 24, 2015

"Efficacy of Bright Light Treatment, Fluoxetine, and the Combination in Patients With Nonseasonal Major Depressive Disorder," JAMA Psychiatry 2016;73(1):56-63

"Therapeutic Observation of Acupuncture for Depressive Insomnia," Shanghai Journal of Acupuncture and Moxibustion 2014; 6: 539-541

"Acupuncture Rivals Antidepressants For Insomnia And Depression," Health CMI (www.healthcmi.com) 2/13/2016

Part 8: Natural Answers for an Ironclad Immune System

"Influence of Epicuticular Physicochemical Properties on Porcine Rotavirus Adsorption to 24 Leafy Green Vegetables and Tomatoes." PLoS One. 2015 Jul 16;10(7):e0132841.

http://pdf.usaid.gov/pdf_docs/Pnacy849.pdf

http://nwhort.org/wp-content/uploads/2015/07/FreshFruitLabelingManual-rev-070115.pdf

https://www.ewg.org/foodnews/summary.php

Martineau AR, et al. Vitamin D3 supplementation in patients with chronic obstructive pulmonary disease (ViDiCO): a multicentre, double-blind, randomised controlled trial. *The Lancet Respiratory Medicine*, 2014; DOI:10.1016/S2213-2600(14)70255-3.

American Lung Association. Chronic Obstructive Pulmonary Disease (COPD) Fact Sheet. http://www.lung.org/lung-disease/copd/resources/facts-figures/COPD-Fact-Sheet.html. Accessed December 17, 2014.

"The relationship between cold temperature and risk of ischemic stroke in patients with atrial fibrillation." Eur Heart J (2015) 36 (suppl 1).

"How cold is too cold: the effect of seasonal temperature variation on risk of STEMI." Eur Heart J (2015) 36 (suppl 1).

"The relationship between the environmental factors and severity of clinical status and short-term prognosis for the patients with non-ST elevation acute coronary syndromes." Eur Heart J (2015) 36 (suppl 1).

"Echinaforce Hotdrink versus Oseltamivir in Influenza: A randomized, double-blind, double dummy, multicenter, non-inferiority clinical trial."http://dx.doi.org/10.1016/j.curtheres.2015.04.001.

The American Heart Association. Learn About Influenza. (n.d.). Retrieved 2015, from http://www.lung.org/lung-disease/influenza/in-depth-resources/pneumonia-fact-sheet.html

http://www.cdc.gov/vaccines/vpd-vac/shingles/hcp-vaccination.htm

http://www.cdc.gov/vaccines/schedules/hcp/imz/adult.html

"Behaviorally Assessed Sleep and Susceptibility to the Common Cold." *Sleep.*2015 Jan 17. pii: sp-00619-

https://sleepfoundation.org/sleep-polls-data/other-polls/2013-international-bedroom-poll

"Environmental disruption of the circadian clock leads to altered sleep and immune responses in mouse." *Brain Behav Immun.* 2015 Jul;47:14-23.

"Safety and efficacy profile of *Echinacea purpurea* to prevent common cold episodes: a randomized, double-blind, placebo-controlled trial." *Evid Based Complement Alternat Med.* 2012:841315. Epub 2012 Sep 16

"Antibiotic resistance," Centers for Disease Control (www.cdc.gov) 9/16/2013

"Clostridium difficile Infection," N Engl J Med 2015; 372:1539-1548

Part 9: Natural ways to Nurture Your Health

"Plasma 25-Hydroxyvitamin D Levels and Risk of Incident Hypertension Among Young Women," Hypertension Nov 2008;52(5):828-32

"Phenolic acids of the two major blueberry species in the US Market and their antioxidant and anti-inflammatory activities." Plant Foods Hum Nutr. 2015 Mar;70(1):56-62.

"Anti-inflammatory effect of the blueberry anthocyanins malvidin-3-glucoside and malvidin-3-galactoside in endothelial cells." Molecules. 2014 Aug 21;19(8):12827-41.

"Anthocyanins and phenolic acids from a wild blueberry (Vaccinium angustifolium) powder counteract lipid accumulation in THP-1-derived macrophages." Eur J Nutr. 2015 Jan 17.

"Daily blueberry consumption improves blood pressure and arterial stiffness in postmenopausal women with pre- and stage 1-hypertension: a randomized, double-blind, placebo-controlled clinical trial." J Acad Nutr Diet. 2015 Mar;115(3):369-77.

"Blueberry treatment decreased D-galactose-induced oxidative stress and brain damage in rats." Metab Brain Dis. 2015 Jun;30(3):793-802.

"Six weeks daily ingestion of whole blueberry powder increases natural killer cell counts and reduces arterial stiffness in sedentary males and females." Nutr Res. 2014 Jul;34(7):577-84.

"Anthocyanins from fermented berry beverages inhibit inflammation-related adiposity response in vitro." J Med Food. 2015 Apr;18(4):489-96.

"The Effects of Wild Blueberry Consumption on Plasma Markers and Gene Expression Related to Glucose Metabolism in the Obese Zucker Rat." J Med Food. 2014 Nov 10. [Epub ahead of print].

"Wild Blueberry (Vaccinium angustifolium Ait.) Polyphenols Target Fusobacterium nucleatum and the Host Inflammatory Response: Potential Innovative Molecules for Treating Periodontal Diseases." *Journal of Agricultural and Food Chemistry*, 2015; 63 (31): 6999.

"Baobab food products: a review on their composition and nutritional value."Crit Rev Food Sci Nutr. 2009 Mar;49(3):254-74.

USDA National Nutrient Database for Standard Reference Release 27http://ndb.nal.usda.gov/ndb/search/list.

"The use of photochemiluminescence for the measurement of the integral antioxidant capacity of baobab products." Food Chemistry Volume 102, Issue 4, 2007, Pages 1352–1356.

"The polyphenol-rich baobab fruit (Adansonia digitata L.) reduces starch digestion and glycemic response in humans." Nutr Res. 2013 Nov;33(11):888-96.

"Vitamin D deficiency and mortality risk in the general population: a meta-analysis of prospective cohort studies," *Am J Clin Nutr* 2013 97: 782-793

"Vitamins for Chronic Disease Prevention in Adults: : Scientific Review," *JAMA*2002; 287(23): 3,116-3,126 2 "Vitamins for Chronic Disease Prevention in Adults: : Clinical Applications," *JAMA* 2002; 287(23): 3,127-3,129

"Alternative therapy produces intriguing results in some heart patients but many questions remain." American Heart Association Late-Breaking Clinical Trial Report. November 4, 2012.

Micozzi, MS, *Fundamentals of Complementary & Altenative Medicine*, 2010, Elsevier Health Sciences

CalorieKing. Calories in Banana Chips.http://www.calorieking.com/foods/search.php?keywords=banana+chips&go=Go. Accessed June 16, 2014.

CalorieKing. Calories in Energy Bars. http://www.calorieking.com/calories-in-energy+bars.html. Accessed June 16, 2014.

CalorieKing. Hodgson Mill Apple & More Muesli Cereal, dry.http://www.calorieking.com/foods/calories-in-breakfast-cereals-to-be-cooked-apple-more-muesli-dry_f-ZmlkPTE4MzAyMA.html. Accessed June 16, 2014.

National Resources Defense Council. Guide to Mercury in Sushi.http://www.nrdc.org/health/effects/mercury/sushi.asp. Accessed June 16, 2014.

Lowenstein, JH, et al. DNA barcodes reveal species-specific mercury levels in tuna sushi that pose a health risk to consumers. 21 April 2010 doi: 10.1098/rsbl.2010.0156 Biol. Lett.

CalorieKing. Calories in Trail Mix. Average All Brands, Trail Mix: Regular, with Chocolate Chips, Unsalted Nuts & Seeds.http://www.calorieking.com/foods/calories-in-trail-mix-regular-with-chocolate-chips-unsalted-nuts-seeds_f-ZmlkPTYxNDg5.html. Accessed June 16, 2014.

About the Author

Marc S. Micozzi, M.D., Ph.D.

In his 35-year career, physician, medical anthropologist and epidemiologist Marc S. Micozzi M.D., Ph.D., has accomplished something no other physician has been able to achieve.

He thrust the STAGGERING PROOF of complementary alternative therapies in the faces of mainstream medicine AND DEMANDED THEY LISTEN. In fact, some of the world's most recognized natural research—on things like lycopene, lutein, brassica vegetables, and excess iron—would not even exist without his courage to stand up for true science.

His medical career is all but unrivaled—especially given his vast and unique mixture of experience within mainstream medicine and complementary and alternative medicine (CAM).

Dr. Micozzi was the founding editor-in-chief of the first U.S. journal in Complementary and Alternative Medicine and organized and edited the first U.S. textbook in the field, *Fundamentals of Complementary & Integrative Medicine* in 1996, continuously in print for 20 years, now it its 5th edition. He has published nearly 300 articles in medical literature and is the author or editor of over 40 books.

As the Senior Investigator for cancer prevention at the National Cancer Institute, Dr. Micozzi published the original research on diet, nutrition, and chronic disease. He continued this line of research as the Associate Director of the Armed Forces Institute of Pathology and Director of the National Museum of Health and Medicine.

He has served as the Executive Director of the College of Physicians of Philadelphia (the same city where he completed medical and graduate training at the University of Pennsylvania).

In recent years, Dr. Micozzi has served as the Founding Director of the Policy Institute for Integrative Medicine, working to educate policy makers, the health professions, and the general public about the opportunities for integrative medicine and the need for clean, clear science within our modern medical establishment.

As Editor of his monthly newsletter *Insiders' Cures*, Dr. Micozzi's message of taking what's rightfully yours is already changing the lives of people just like you…

Dr. Micozzi has written or edited over 40 books, including (with

Michael Jawer), *The Spiritual Anatomy of Emotion* and *Your Emotional Type: Key to the Therapies That Will Work for You*. He was the founding editor-in-chief of the first U.S. journal on the subject of CAM (in 1994), and he organized and edited the first U.S. textbook, *Fundamentals of Complementary & Alternative Medicine*, now going into it's fifth edition.

"*The Spiritual Anatomy* of Emotion presents a unique and arresting view of such topics as mind, body, memory, illness, perception, and emotion. The authors show us an altogether novel way of understanding who we are and what we're about. There's more to being human than we ever imagine, and this book is an excellent road map for anyone who wants to take that journey."

ERIC LESKOWITZ, M.D.,
Department of Psychiatry, Harvard Medical School

"*Your Emotional Type*, may be the Rosetta Stone we've been waiting for—a code for matching a particular therapy to a particular patient. Micozzi and Jawer… have found gold."

LARRY DOSSEY, M.D.
Author of *Healing Words: The Power and Prayer and the Practice of Medicine* and *The Power of Premonitions*

"By helping patients understand the connection between their personality type, their symptoms, and treatment choices, Jawer and Micozzi help patients become more informed consumers of alternative health care."

ILENE A. SERLIN,
Psychologist and Dance Movement Therapist

You can read more about all of Dr. Micozzi's titles and purchase them online at www.drmicozzi.com.

D riving through the streets of North Berkeley in the spring of 2020, I saw a scene right out of the post-apocalyptic Sci-Fi film *On the Beach* (1959). I imagined myself as Gregory Peck observing the eerie evacuated streets of San Francisco through his submarine's periscope off Fisherman's Wharf. Except for a few isolated souls who were either homeless, in denial, or shopping for essentials, it looked like a neutron bomb had wiped out North Berkeley's local population, leaving only structures standing. It seemed incomprehensible, surreal, like those early 20th century Giorgio de Chirico paintings of empty, haunted Italian streets and plazas. How did we get here?

Covid revealed itself in increasingly painful incre-ments. First there had been travel advisories in February. Then when the first Covid case was diagnosed in Berkeley on March 3, social distancing was recommended. By March 16, stay-at-home orders were issued in several Bay Area juris-dictions.

I took these shots on April 9 in North Berkeley. Grégoire's on Cedar Street near Shattuck Avenue (left) is only open for take-out. A sign explains their social distancing requirements. To the right, on the 1700 block of Shattuck, local shoppers on bikes are stocking up on beer, a Covid essential for many.

Were we sheltering in place or locked down? The terminology was not yet set. One term seemed less severe than the other, but essentially they meant the same thing. Still, the CDC did not yet believe face masks were necessary when leaving one's home for essential activities.

On March 26 most construction projects were cancelled, including the remodeling project just started at my home. A delay of two months was predicted, as were spikes in material and labor costs. Stay-at-home orders were extended and face coverings were finally required of everyone on April 26. Then the wildfires came, and with them toxic smoke beyond anyone's experience. As if a global pandemic were not enough, California had to cope with the worst fire season in its history. One could not avoid the poisonous "bad air" fallacy of the pre-scientific miasma theory of disease. The August Complex fire was labeled a "gigafire", the first ever, with more than one million acres burned. Intense thunderstorms in August sparked many of the 367 known fires at the time.

A heat wave then arrived in early September and Santa Ana winds caused the August Complex to grow to more than twice the size of the 2018 Mendocino Complex. Previous years of drought in California had led to a forest die-off caused by too much moisture being taken out of the soil and too little rain going back in. These climate change conditions provided the kindling for the fire and smoke storms of 2018-2020.

The smoky, obliterated bay view from my Berkeley Hills home on September 9.

Art history in the making: The extraordinary orange-colored miasmic haze today, September 9, gave Mother Nature a new palette color – smoky orange. Imagine an Impressionist artist like Claude Monet painting his *Impression, Sunrise* in San Francisco in 2020 instead of Le Havre in 1872. Would the term Impressionism have been coined? What would this alternate version of the painting be called – *Smoky, Sunrise*? I don't think an art movement based on smoky air would, um, catch fire.

Smoky, Sunrise. Monet/Harris (1872/2020).

Impression, Sunrise. Claude Monet (1872).

And speaking of catching fire, when did Smokey Bear arrive on the scene? It started in the 1940s as a campaign to prevent man-made forest and grassland fires in the US. Smokey's slogan was, "Remember…Only YOU Can Prevent Forest Fires." How quaint. What would Smokey say today as I brace for fires to reach my home in the Berkeley Hills? Maybe, "Is your emergency to-go bag ready?"

Loimos and the whole Greek catastrophe: The elemental disruptions of air, fire, water and land that accompanied Covid in 2020 – what we blandly label "climate change" – render the Egyptian plagues recounted during Passover's Seder ritual (frogs, locusts, boils, etc.) small potatoes compared to the fiery chaos, excessive heat, violent storms, floods and infection surges that would ravage bodies and communities here and abroad.

From the great film, *Zorba the Greek* (1964), Anthony Quinn's memorable expression "the whole catastrophe" seems an apt expression, but it doesn't really do justice to the whole Covid catastrophe. The Greek concept of *loimos* (or *limos*) comes closer. The term roughly translates as "pestilence", but it goes further. Here is the chorus' description of Thebes at the beginning of *Oedipus Rex* (also known as *Oedipus Tyrannus*) by Sophocles:

Thebes is dying A blight on the fresh crops and the rich pastures, cattle sicken and die, and the women die in labor, children stillborn, and the plague, the fiery god of fever hurls down on the city, his lightning slashing through us – raging plague in all its vengeance, devastating the house of Cadmus! And black Death luxuriates in the raw, wailing miseries of Thebes.

The scholar Robert Parker applies *loimos* to the Thebes of Sophocles in his book *Miasma: Pollution and Purification in Early Greek Religion* (1983):

The ways in which divine anger against a community could be expressed were diverse. At the beginning of Sophocles' Oedipus Tyrannus, Thebes is afflicted in three ways – the crops have failed, women and animals cannot bring forth their young, a plague is raging... The name for this whole complex of disasters is loimos, which is thus much broader than 'plague' by which it is commonly rendered.

Medieval man – doctors, scholars and priests – was no better than the ancients at explaining or responding to the devastation caused by pestilence. Leading up to the emergence of the plague in 14th century Europe, one Flemish cleric, quoted in Ziegler's *The Black Death*, sounds a lot like Sophocles describing the afflictions terrorizing Thebes in *Oedipus Rex*:

> *In the East, hard by Greater India, in a certain province, horrors and unheard of tempests overwhelmed the whole province for the space of three days. On the first day there was a rain of frogs, serpents, lizards, scorpions, and many venomous beasts of that sort. On the second, thunder was heard, and lightning and sheets of fire fell upon the earth, mingled with hailstones of marvelous size; which slew almost all, from the greatest even to the least. On the third day there fell fire from heaven and stinking smoke, which slew all that were left of men and beasts, and burned up all the cities and towns in those parts.*

I don't know about frogs, serpents, lizards and scorpions, but there have been rat invasions here in Berkeley caused by the fires raging around us. Coyotes and other critters, too, are coming to town, looking for water and food. Given emerging climate change disasters here and around the country and world, on top of the pandemic, the Greek *loimos* is the perfect term, if not the explanation, for our "whole catastrophe".

55

Oedipus vs. Trump. December 2020. This image emerged after reading an article in the *Los Angeles Times* by the theater critic, Charles McNulty, comparing the drama of Trump with that of Oedipus Rex. You can mix and match the terms with the two characters to come up with a winner in the *Most Tragic Ruler* category, "tragic" in the classical and/ or pathetic sense.

Tragic Trump, Oedipus Rex et al: I can live without theaters – cinematic and live – at least temporarily. The Covid/Trump show on TV, radio and the internet more than fills our drama void, though the loss of buttered popcorn nibbled in dark rooms filled with anonymous souls and magical images is hard to swallow. Dramatists, filmmakers, artists, poets and novelists will have years, decades, even centuries to put a frame around our catastrophe. And they will no doubt make use of narratives from plagues past – real and literary – to put 2020 into perspective, more persuasively than I am doing now.

In the Old Testament, the biblical plagues that fell on Egypt are linked to Pharaoh's refusal to heed Moses' demand to release the enslaved Jews. I know this from my brief tenure at Saturday school (the Jewish version of Sunday school), but I'm just learning now that some scientists believe these biblical blights were based on real ones triggered by a gigantic climate-changing volcanic eruption on the Greek island of Santorini. Who knew?

Reading up on plagues past, I have yet to find anything in the history of the mother of all plagues – Europe's Black Death – that offers a merger of contagion and ruler comparable to Pharaoh and the biblical plagues or, fast forward, Donald Trump and Covid-19. The bubonic plague that killed more than one third of Europe's population – and 20 percent of the world's – in the 14th century was attributed, at that time, not to any ruler (king or pope) but to sinful humans (especially Jews) and a resulting corrupted miasmatic atmosphere.

In the 20th century, President Woodrow Wilson was stigmatized by his handling of the so-called Spanish flu of 1918 because he hid information about the pandemic from the public, as Trump did with Covid-19. His commitment to fight World War I at all costs contributed to the high death toll from the epidemic. Some would label this a crime, but he wasn't hiding the threat for purely personal or political motives, as Trump did. Wilson, again like Trump, contracted the virus and survived. However, he was not a one-man super spreader event like The Donald. Wilson was, in my view, a flawed president under pressure from a still-raging world war, not a criminal plague agent and denier.

Shifting back in time to ancient Rome, Nero famously fiddled while the city burned. I'm tempted to try to caricature Trump golfing while Americans die from Covid, but I'm sure that image already exists somewhere in the pages of *The New York Times*, the *Washington Post* or *The New Yorker* magazine. Yet Nero's urban fire does not conjure up the destruction of a plague proper or the Greeks' idea of a super pestilence, *loimos*. Trump and his grotesqueries trump Nero.

Socio-pathetic Trump has been compared to other malignant kings, tyrants, presidents and scoundrels besides Pharaoh and Nero – Mad King George, Richard Nixon and Adolf Hitler come to mind. In literature there is Shakespeare's Macbeth, Sophocles' Oedipus, Alfred Jarry's King Ubu and Sinclair Lewis' Berzelius "Buzz" Windrip. In line with Covid's reported (possible) origins in infected bats, Vlad the Impaler (Vlad Dracula of Transylvania, inspiration for Bram Stoker's batty Count Dracula) comes close to Trump-level pathology. On the other hand, Vlad boasted legitimate royal lineage and, it is claimed, real executive abilities – positive traits lacking in our bilious, bulbous, bumbling, billionaire bagman.

Then there's Henry VIII. I find it hilarious (and macabre) that one of Trump's co-conspirators, Steve Bannon, has suggested putting Trump opponents' heads on pikes, as was done, Bannon notes in an interview, in Tudor England. Trump does resemble the most famous Tudor king, whose addiction to eating, spending and philandering were, in fact, the least of his sins. But in truth, Trump is no Henry VIII, whose virtues in his prime were real.

This viral meme was re-tweeted by Trump in March of 2020.

Trump's crimes against women (the ones we know about) don't reach the level of Henry VIII's beheading of two wives, nor to the incest of Oedipus with Jocasta. But what about the high crimes of patricide and regicide? Trump's attempted take down of President-elect Joe Biden echoes Oedipus' murder of his father, King Laius. One could write a college level essay on the Freudian symbolism of Trump's efforts to "kill" our new American father figure (with references to Trump's issues with his own father). But, as the Los Angeles Times theater critic, Charles McNulty, put it in his article *President Trump vs. Oedipus Rex* (March 26, 2020), "Donald Trump is no Oedipus".

Oedipus, unaware of his high crimes and misdemeanors, had the *orcheis* (courage or balls in Greek) to take responsibility for the Theban miasma after learning, no, demanding the truth about Laius' death from the blind seer, Tiresias. Not so, Trump with Covid. In retrospect, his high crime was having known the truth about the virus from the get-go and hiding it from the country – thanks for sharing, Mr. Woodward. McNulty's article sums up the Trump/Oedipus/pandemic connection brilliantly:

As the world confronts a new pandemic, it behooves us to consider why the cornerstone text of Western literature is a play about a ruler discovering himself while confronting a plague. Nothing cuts our species down to size quite like a scourge… Unfortunately, the last thing Trump wishes to be is a tragic hero…

The drama of *Oedipus Rex* seems the closest comparison of all the great plague/ruler narratives – historical or literary – to that of Trump Rex. The shared backdrop of an interwoven, bio-political plague binds them closely together. Tragic Trump may be – in the pathetic sense of the word. Tragicomic may come even closer. But as a tragic hero à la Oedipus who accepts responsibility and punishment for his crimes? Not a Greek meatball's chance in hell.

~MIASMA BATH BLEND~
LAVENDER & MINT-INFUSED
SALT WATER

Ancient Greek-Style White House Cleanse, January 2021. Long before medieval plague doctors were using sweet smelling flowers and herbs in their pointed birdlike face masks to filter plague miasma, the Greeks were burning incense in temples to purify the miasmatic air, expel demons and appease the Gods.

Making light of the dark: Following the November election, the GSA (General Services Administration) described a "much needed deep cleaning treatment" for the White House before President Biden moved in (*The Daily Beast*, December 9). This would "thoroughly clean and disinfect" surfaces, drapes, furniture, etc., while a "disinfectant misting service" would purge the air of any coronavirus residue from Trump's departed staff and family.

Not good enough, as far as I am concerned. What the White House needs, more than germ (and Trump) removal, is spiritual purification. Yes, something has to be done about Trump's vibes – or, as the ancient Greeks might have described it, the miasmic shroud that darkens the White House.

For the Greeks, countering miasma involved not only herbal cleansing practices (akin to native American "smudging") and religious prayer but often, ritual animal slaughter and/or the expulsion of scapegoats from the community, practices known as *pharmakós* in Greek. It was thought that by sacrificing or casting out a ritual scapegoat, the contamination could be expelled.

According, again, to Robert Parker, the scapegoats were usually beggars or criminals but could also be " ...a person of especially high value – the fairest virgin in the land, the king's daughter; or even the king himself." Sounds to me a lot like the Trumps being booted out of Washington, D.C. and making their way to Mar-a-Lago. Little Barron Trump in this scenario can play the role of fairest virgin. As for the cleansing of the White House, I think it advisable, as my drawing suggests, to bring in authentic Greek or American shamans to perform a purge of the premises. Our White House's miasma requires more than superficial American hygiene to remove the darkness of the past four years.

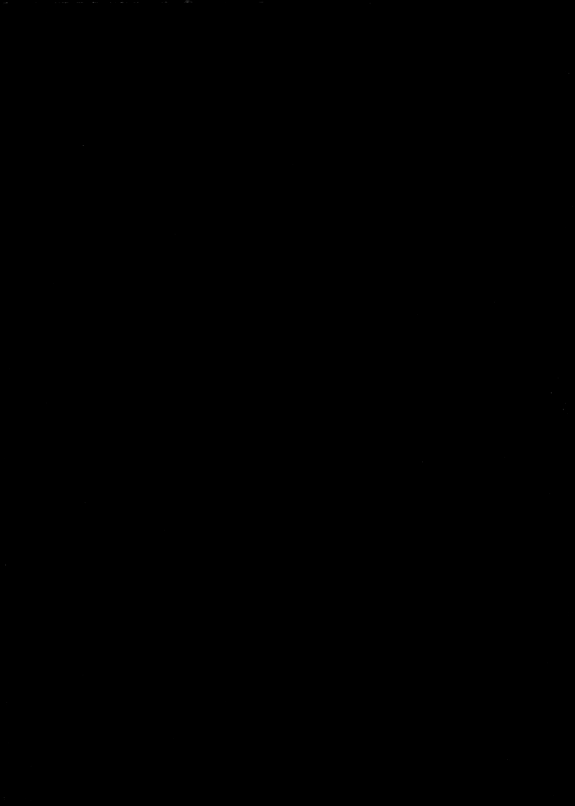

MY MIASMA MASK COLLECTION

My miasma masks, all drawn in the spring and summer of 2020 when we were trying to get used to wearing them, take protection to another level – fashionable, functional and fanciful. But are masks here to stay, along with Covid-19 and its variants and ever newer viral and bacterial invaders?* If so, then why must masks be so boringly utilitarian? I'm certainly not alone in wondering why so many otherwise well dressed folks (including me) are sporting those awful disposable pale blue, 5-ply, ear-loop medical masks. We need a Coco Chanel of Covid (*Cocovid Chanel?*). Can't we at least have emerald, mustard, lavender and other tastefully colored versions? When fashion gurus tell us that stripes, plaids, pastels or florals are in this year, why shouldn't masks follow suit? If designers are adding beads, semi-precious stones and sequins to their fashion collections, why not include coordinated mask collections? Some have tried, but will they last?

If you follow design and fashion news, as I occasionally do, Covid is having a huge impact on the design world. A recent article in the *Financial Times of London* (Summer 2021) reports the merging of fashion and interior design inspired by our housebound, comfort-hungry Covid lives. One line of comfortable "puffy" sofas, influenced by a fashion designer's quilted clothing collection, is highlighted. But no mention of masks. Why not puffy masks?

Will protective masks take their place alongside standard fashion and status accessories? Hats began as functional necessities to ward off the elements from above – heat, rain, snow, wind-blown debris and pigeon droppings. Later they became status symbols. The taller the hat, the higher the status. Head covering styles announced particular trades, governmental positions and religious affiliations. Kings and queens had crowns, chefs had toques (and more recently ball caps), soldiers had helmets, priests had birettas and rabbis had yarmulkes. You are what you wear. Same with scarves, gloves and shoes. First function, then fashion. Will masks follow this same pattern? Time will tell, but my guess is yes.

* "Hold onto your masks. They are going to be a permanent part of your wardrobe." Quoted from an article in *The New York Times*, August 5, 2021.

THE SAFE NEW POST-COVID WHITE TABLECLOTH DINING EXPERIENCE

ZIP + MASK + BIB

BLACK ELASTIC EAR GRIPS

DOUBLE LAYER LINEN MASK
REPURPOSED TABLECLOTHS

HEAVY-DUTY ZIPPER INSERT
IDEAL FOR EASY ACCESS

INTEGRATED BIB EXTENDER

THESE 100% RECYCLED
LINEN FACE MASK &
BIB COMBOS FOR
SAFE DINING OUT ARE AVAILABLE AT
RESTAURANT SUPPLY OUTLETS NEAR YOU

LJH 4/2020

Bib Gourmand. April 2020.

At the dinner table: As Covid began to close down our lives in the spring of 2020, there was already talk of a crisis in the world of high end white tablecloth dining. Higher labor costs were eating into narrow profit margins at the top of the food chain long before our current labor scarcity pushed costs even higher. Talk of more casual dining "fast casual" was common in the food media well before Covid struck. In my Bib Gourmand drawing I saw a silver lining in the movement away from glamour and pretention in the food world — a symbolic repurposing of the white tablecloth as a combo linen mask and bib. I hadn't yet thought of the connection to the Michelin Guide's lower priced Bib Gourmand restaurant category when I drew the image, but it popped up and I've named the drawing accordingly.

Your Face Mask. June 2020.

YOUR FACE MASK™
SILK SCREENED WITH YOUR
NOSE AND YOUR MOUTH

LSH 6/20

Your Face Mask: I saw a smattering of one-of-a-kind, hand sewn cloth face masks on the streets during the early days of Covid, but their individuality did not solve my problem. Who is that person behind the mask? When I run into folks I know, or should know, I'm often clueless. That's because masks mask two of the three key identifiers for facial recognition—the nose and the mouth. Psychologists have studied how faces are recognized in different cultures and the common denominator (at least with infants) is that it takes three facial features to trigger recognition. Eyes alone are not enough. I propose a cloth mask with a silk-screened image of *your* nose and *your* mouth taken from your high-resolution photo.

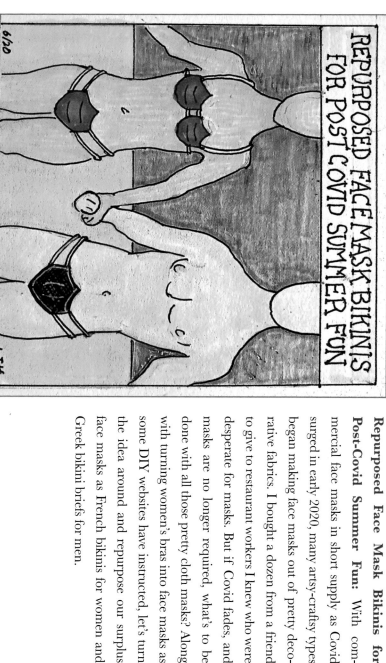

Repurposed Face Mask Bikinis for Post-Covid Summer Fun:

With commercial face masks in short supply as Covid surged in early 2020, many artsy-craftsy types began making face masks out of pretty decorative fabrics. I bought a dozen from a friend to give to restaurant workers I knew who were desperate for masks. But if Covid fades, and masks are no longer required, what's to be done with all those pretty cloth masks? Along with turning women's bras into face masks as some DIY websites have instructed, let's turn the idea around and repurpose our surplus face masks as French bikinis for women and Greek bikini briefs for men.

Introducing the Face Pack:

This face mask offers increased utility. While it protects against germs, it provides storage for a variety of small items carried in fanny packs, pockets and purses. The oversized silver zippers mounted in a breathable grey fabric offer stylish access. The lower straps anchor the Face Pack firmly to the torso, providing support and comfort.

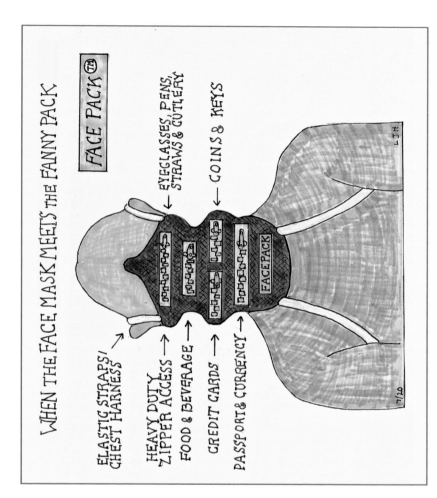

WHEN THE FACE MASK MEETS THE FANNY PACK

FACE PACK ™

ELASTIC STRAPS/
CHEST HARNESS

HEAVY DUTY
ZIPPER ACCESS →

FOOD & BEVERAGE →

CREDIT CARDS →

PASSPORT & CURRENCY →

EYEGLASSES, PENS,
STRAWS & CUTLERY
↓

COINS & KEYS
↓

FACEPACK

7/20

LJH

Face Pack. July 2020.

IV   PANDEMICS AND POLITICS

We peruse the latest copy of The New Yorker or The Onion, embedding political cartoons as a means of entertainment, when in fact they are powerful forms that reify social values and set agendas.

—Jacob Steere-Williams in
Personifying Pestilence: How Political Cartoons Shape Our Views of Disease

HUMPTY TRUMPTY
SAT ON A WALL,
HUMPTY TRUMPTY
HAD A GREAT FALL,
ALL THE REPUBLICAN
HORSES, AND ALL THE
REPUBLICAN MEN,
COULDN'T PUT TRUMPTY
TOGETHER AGAIN.

Humpty Trumpty. June 2016. When I came up with this variation on the old English nursery rhyme during the presidential primaries in 2016, perhaps my first-ever political cartoon, it seemed unthinkable that Donald Trump could ever make it to the White House.

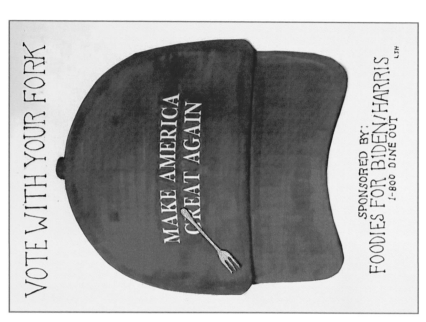

VOTE WITH YOUR FORK

MAKE AMERICA GREAT AGAIN

SPONSORED BY:
FOODIES FOR BIDEN/HARRIS
1-800 DINE OUT

LJH

Make America Eat Again. September 2020.

I have no serious affinity or ambition (and little talent) for traditional political cartooning, but our interwoven viruses – Trump and Covid – have pushed me in that direction. The post-election success of Biden's vaccine roll-out slowed the plague's conjoined evils, but neither is truly defeated. Both Trump and Covid appear to be endemic and beg for the cartoonist's dark exorcisms. Trump's hat seemed like my logical starting point for some visual fun and catharsis before the election.

My appropriation of Trump's MAGA hat (and the food activist "Vote with your fork" slogan from several years ago) for a pro-Biden election poster posited a progressive American foodie constituency that supports the idea that a post-pandemic recovery of the restaurant industry can be best accomplished by a Biden/Harris presidency. Altering Trump's campaign slogan from "Great Again" to "Eat Again" had a certain logic in the context of our at-risk restaurant community.

My MAGA hat project has been, more or less, a complete bust. Appropriating Trump's political symbol to showcase one of the pandemic's most serious economic and cultural threats – restaurant industry collapse – felt palliative to me, a parodic purgation, a casting out of hateful demons aligned with Trump's political base and moral baseness.

The failure of this graphic gesture to capture support on social media was based, it appears, on my underestimation of how verboten Trump's MAGA cap had become for the left. On the political right the hat is sacrosanct, a cult fetish object; for the left, it's vile excrement. When I offered hand-altered hats for sale in September (I had bought six) at $250 a pop to benefit the Biden/Harris campaign, no one stepped up. Note, however, how Larry David wore his MAGA hat in a 2016 *Curb Your Enthusiasm* episode to keep people away he didn't like. In that sense, the project has been an ironic success – in reverse. It has kept away people I *do* like.

The feedback on my altered MAGA hat was so negative that, at the suggestion of a friend, I had a graphic artist change the color from red to blue. The hope was that this would soften the image's stigma and create demand. At the same time, the letters "GR" in the word GREAT were removed from behind the fork handle to clarify the new slogan's "EAT". But this sanitization has transformed a symbolic exorcism of Trump into a symbolic castration of me. All this reminds me of the basic rule for artists, and especially cartoonists: Place your bets and let the chips fall where they may.

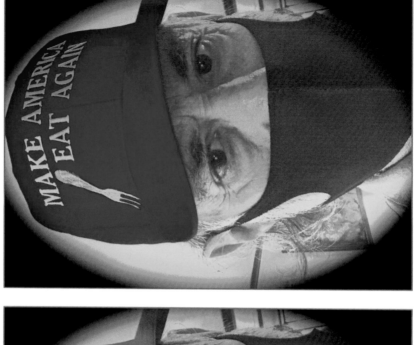

A sanitized MAGA hat exorcism. October 2020.

A selfie with repurposed MAGA hat. September 2020.

75

On the eve of the election there was a serious concern in Democratic circles about whether it would proceed in an orderly fashion without interference from aggressive Republican poll watchers seeking to suppress voting. Berkeley was not considered a target, but I did contemplate volunteering my services at the local voting site. Instead, I drew this image of a Berkeley poll watcher displaying real and made up foodie memes and puns, and posted it online. There were a few mixed reviews, but mostly silence. As with my MAGA hat images, playing with the Black Lives Matter slogan is unacceptable for many. And the T-shirt's foodie Frenchification of QAnon was labeled "too cute" by one responder, and "a stretch" by another. As stated earlier, my cartoonist's mantra: Place your bets and let the chips fall where they may.

Oral arguments: Viral plagues seem so much more insidious than a virus. You can kill a bacterium more easily than a virus. When I read a *New Yorker* article by David Joselit (June 5, 2020) titled *Virus as Metaphor*, I began to understand our merged Covid/Trump catastrophe not so much in cultural and political terms but biologically. Trump has "legitimized", writes Joselit, "a relation to knowledge that is viral rather than evidence-based." Joselit quotes William Burroughs from *The Ticket That Exploded*: "The flu virus may once have been a healthy lung cell. It is now a parasitic organism that invades and damages the lungs." Our election was about a once healthy body politic under attack by a parasitic organism called Trump.

I am reminded from my research for *The Book of Garlic* in the 1970s of the ancient Greek Doctrine of Signatures. It states that herbs, nuts and vegetables that resemble human body parts can treat ailments of those parts. Walnuts, for example, have the signature of the human head (skull and brain) and can treat related ailments. Perhaps a variation of this pseudo-scientific doctrine is more plausible: Noxious pathogens can share a "signature" with the body part or organ they infect. My drawing of Trump's infected tongue makes the case.

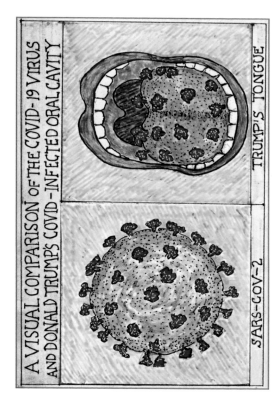

A Visual Comparison. November 2020.

Trump as virus: It seemed a bit of divine retribution when Trump caught "the flu" in October of 2020, and I felt, as many did, a burst of schadenfreude watching him suffer. Paradoxically, rather than underscoring his human vulnerability and unforgiveable denial of the pandemic's seriousness, Trump's bout with Covid strengthened his hold over his minions. He was Covid's ultimate and simultaneous survivor and denier. In purely political terms, and outside the Greek dimension of Sophoclean miasma, Trump was routinely labeled by the "fake news" media as a fascistic strongman, crime family boss and authoritarian wannabe.

There were also critical explorations of Trump's relationship to pop culture narratives of superheroes and villains. Was the Covid virus Trump's kryptonite? As with kryptonite's effect on Superman, the virus weakened Trump but couldn't destroy him. After returning home from his successful treatment in the hospital, he reportedly intended to reveal a Superman shirt under his dress shirt during his presentation from the White House's Truman Balcony. Perhaps, in a rare act of self-control, he decided against it. Or — I'm guessing here — Trump's aides couldn't find a Superman shirt large enough for him. I'm sure, however, that the irony of exposing himself on the Tru-man Balcony would have been lost on Mr. Tru-mp.

Batman motifs emerged in the media, too. Actor/artist Jim Carrey got it right in 2018 with his terrific caricature of Trump as The Joker, Batman's evil nemesis. These are all colorful and amusing ways to capture the pathology of Trump. But equating Trump and Trumpism with the biology of viruses seems the most appropriate diagnostic metaphor for exposing the danger we face, as my chart (opposite) makes clear.

THE TRUMP VIRUS*

- The word "virus" comes from the Latin word for poison. (Trump is a deadly toxin in the body politic.)

- Because viruses carry some but not all of the elements of life – genetic material but no cell structure – they are considered organisms "at the edge of life". (A suitable description of Trump.)

- Some viruses can evade immune responses and result in chronic infections. (Trump is our politic's "Teflon Don" that not even a lost election can stop.)

- A host virus's genetic material can be passed on "vertically" to offspring for many generations. (In process via Trump's brood.)

- To control a virus, the host must be identified and separated from the community. (Off to Mar-a-Lago, Trump's social media accounts canceled.)

- Viral epidemics and pandemics usually return for a second and more lethal wave until herd immunity can be established by the affected community. (Trump's possible second wave presidency will certainly trump his first.)

*My chart is based on some very basic properties of viruses gleaned from the internet and vetted by a biochemist. I invite a deeper analysis by qualified experts.

When I posted on Facebook a caricature of Trump as a lame duck after the election, it inspired the comedian and actor (and, it must be noted, former Cheese Board Collective member), Darryl Henriques to comment on Trump's resemblance to the absurd tyrant, Père Ubu, in Alfred Jarry's 1896 play, *Ubu Roi*. Henriques quoted the great critic of Modernism, Roger Shattuck, from his book, *The Banquet Years*, that was devoured by just about everyone I knew in the 1970s:

…*Ubu has only his appetites, which he displays like virtues. When we try to injure him with our laughter ("satanic" laughter Baudelaire would call it), we discover that his behavior is so abject that we cannot reach him. He does not have traits of either a great hero or a great villain… He remains a threat because he can destroy at will, and the political horrors of the twentieth century make the lesson disturbingly real.*

Fast forward to the political horrors of the early 21st century; Père Ubu/Trump has morphed into a virus.

Our Lame Duck. November 2020. How many people died because Trump refused to wear and promote masks? I've heard estimates as high as 100,000.

Bonfire of the Vanities: When Trump was impeached for a second time, after the January 6 insurrection, I celebrated by performing my version of a 15th century Catholic ritual, the bonfire of the vanities. The story goes that Girolamo Savonarola, the notorious 15th century Florentine monk, collected "sinful objects" including artwork (even paintings by Botticelli), books (including some by Boccaccio), mirrors, dresses and cosmetics, and burned them in public on February 7, 1497. This began an annual Catholic ritual and the expression we still use today. Savonarola's burnt objects were symbolic of the human vanities he preached against. Vanity has been defined, in religious terms, as a form of self-idolatry in which one likens oneself to the greatness of God for the sake of one's own image. This is an excellent description of Trump's narcissism.

The decision to burn Trump's altered vanity hats on January 13 came as a sudden whim. I did not hesitate. I did not even know if they would catch fire. I started with one and it ignited rather easily. I then burned the remaining hats all together, keeping one as a memento of the project. The ritual pleasure was as intense as the blaze. Savonarola knew what he was talking about. *Vanitas vanitatum, et omnia vanitas.*

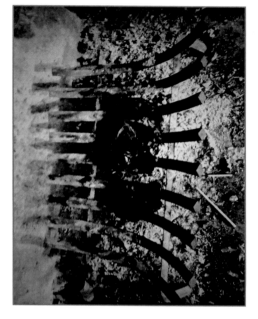

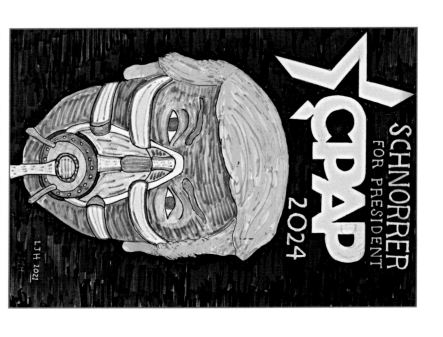

Schnorrer for President. February/July 2021.

Parting shot: Do you have to be Jewish, overweight and a heavy snorer to get this one? I'll explain. I saw Trump on TV speak at CPAC, the Conservative Political Action Conference. This was in February of 2021, in front of an adoring crowd that cheered Trump's tease that he would run again in 2024. Well, one thing led to another and *voilà*: CPAC morphed into CPAP, which is the acronym for the "continuous positive airway pressure" machine that treats sleep apnea (dangerously severe snoring). Combined with the Yiddish word "schnorrer" — meaning, in English, a money-grubbing chiseler — I had another political campaign poster, this one on hold for, God forbid, 2024.

Cartoon coda: As I was putting the final touches on my Trump campaign poster for 2024, I came across some bad news for political cartoonists that I had not heard before: *The New York Times* decided in 2019 to stop publishing single panel political cartoons. Here is what Matt Wuerker, the Pulitzer-winning cartoonist for *Politico*, said about the *Times'* decision:

The collapsing space for political cartoons and satirical commentary because editors don't have the spine to stand up to social-media outrage campaigns is bad for free speech, and bad because political debate benefits from a little humor now and again.

If the window is closing on the art of political cartooning in print media, the timing is terrible. Serious old school print cartoonists couldn't wish for better material than what we see every day in the world of Covid and Trump. I hope that my political images line up with Wuerker's hopes for "a little humor now and again" during a rather humorless time.

A PLAGUE DINER'S DIARY

March 16, 2020 – May 16, 2021

Whether it's chefs digging deep into why they're really in the profession, designers re-envisioning dining spaces, owners revolutionizing their revenue assumptions and models, and all of us looking at how to treat our workers better, there's no going back to the way things were.

— David Chang
Bloomberg Opinion, November 1, 2020

On April 9, 2020, a white sign attached to the locked bamboo gate at Chez Panisse announced, I assume, the restaurant's closure to inside dining. The menu to the right, framed in a glass cabinet, no doubt offered the restaurant's limited take-out menu. But I was too struck by the homeless fellow seated on the steps alongside his rolling cart to care about the postings. His "closed" body language spoke more clearly, more eloquently, and more sadly than any sign could about what was going on at the restaurant, on the street, and in the world. A dark day for me, as my shadow suggests.

M an shall not live by bread alone, says the biblical proverb, somewhat ambiguously. The same can be said about coffee. We break bread and drink coffee (or tea, or wine, or cocktails, or sparkling water) with others – not alone – to nourish both body and soul. Hence the evolution of a café and restaurant culture all across the world that endures the ups and downs of war and peace. Even in Nazi-occupied Paris in the 1940s, restaurants and cafés thrived, serving citizens caffeine and calories for optimal performance, and sociability for emotional and intellectual connection. But during a pandemic there is no collaboration with the enemy and shutdowns are necessary for survival.

After 50 years of sociable eating and drinking out in Berkeley, the Bay Area and beyond – and writing about it – my gastronomic universe came to a halt in March of 2020. So I took to my journal and camera to record this new dining reality, or surreality, as the case may be. Where there is a will, there is a way. And where there is an appetite, there is a meal, even in isolation. These selected entries from my journal document my will and my appetite during a Covid year of eating and drinking, mostly alone, mostly at home.

Bon Appétit!

MARCH 16, 2020

Berkeley is starting to shut down: Yesterday, I brought one of my favorite coffee mugs, a silverplate knife and fork, and a cloth napkin to my still-open morning spot — Saul's Delicatessen. I ordered a cappuccino and a slice of pound cake. I poured the coffee from a Saul's to-go paper cup straight into my ceramic cup. The barista was not allowed to use one of Saul's. The cake was served on a sheet of waxed paper directly onto the napkin I placed on my disinfected table. I was able to leave the exact amount of the bill to minimize shared contact with money. This is crazy!

The morning manager, witnessing my picnic table set up, laughed and asked to take a picture. This was evidently an amusing first, though the day before a fellow came in to eat, she said, wearing a gas mask and rubber suit. I decided to take a picture too, documenting perhaps my last café visit for the foreseeable future. All the cafés in Paris are closed now, according to press reports, and no doubt it's the same all over Europe. Ours are next.

One of my favorite café culture quotes from Thomas Pynchon's *Grav-ity's Rainbow*:

Dialectics, matrices, archetypes all need to connect once in a while, back to some of that proletarian blood, to body odors and senseless screaming across a table, to cheating and last hopes, or else all is dusty Dracularity; the West's ancient curse.

A final picnic at Saul's Deli.

MARCH 22

My solo birthday breakfast: I celebrated my bachelor's birthday this morning with a breakfast that takes me back to my childhood: bacon and eggs. It's the classic American breakfast and the one I loved most as a kid growing up in Los Angeles. (Back in the 90s, the owner of David's Delicatessen in San Francisco complained to me about the challenges of running a Jewish deli in "the land of bacon and eggs".) My older neighbor in LA (not Jewish) shared the same birthday and for years we would celebrate together by splitting a pound of fried bacon. I don't recall if we had the eggs. Bacon was our bond.

A celebratory Covid birthday breakfast at home.

Branded Birthday Breakfast Menu*

- Niman Ranch bacon
- Chino Valley Ranch eggs
- Community Grains wheat toast
- Straus Family Creamery butter
- Peet's coffee

*Although the ingredients here are far superior to those in the 1950s and '60s, does this meal taste any better today than it did then? Yes, if you think about it. No, if you don't.

MARCH 23

Slight of tongue: I find that the boringly repetitive food I am making at home, based on an impoverished pantry and limited shopping, seems more exciting, and even tastes better, if I give the dishes a foreign name. Here is what I ate last week translated via a foreign language translation app into the tongues associated with my usual cooking styles.

Four Simple Dishes, Four Languages, and Vegan Variations

1. Pasta with canned tomatoes, garlic powder and olive oil:

Italian: *Pasta con pomodori in scatola, aglio in polvere e olio d'oliva*
French: *Pâtes aux tomates en conserve, poudre d'ail et huile d'olive*
Spanish: *Pasta con tomates enlatados, ajo en polvo y aceite de oliva*

2. Lamb chops rubbed with cumin and red pepper flakes:

Italian: *Costolette di agnello strofinate con cumino e pepe rosso*
French: *Côtelettes d'agneau enrobées de cumin et de poivron rouge*
Spanish: *Chuletas de cordero frotadas con comino y pimiento rojo*

3. Scrambled eggs with cheddar cheese and green onions:

Italian: *Uova strapazzate con formaggio cheddar e cipolle verdi*
French: *Oeufs brouillés au cheddar et oignons verts*
Spanish: *Huevos revueltos con queso cheddar y cebollas verdes*

4. Leftover roast chicken with boiled rice and pureed zucchini:

Italian: *Avanzi pollo arrosto con bollito con riso e purea di zucchine*
French: *Reste de poulet rôti bouilli avec du riz et de la purée de courgettes*
Spanish: *Sobrantes de pollo asado con hervido con arroz y calabacín puré*

FOR VEGANS: Just add the word "vegan" to each animal protein ingredient, as in the following example. No doubt the "lamb chops" will be made of seasoned tofu:

Vegan lamb chops rubbed with cumin and red pepper flakes:

Italian: *Costolette di agnello vegano strofinate con cumino e pepe rosso*
French: *Côtelettes d'agneau végétalien frottées au cumin et au poivron rouge*
Spanish: *Chuletas de cordero vegano frotadas con comino y pimiento rojo*

MARCH 24

Safe sharing: During the AIDS epidemic we learned to practice safe sex. Now, with the coronavirus pandemic, we need to practice safe sharing. But what are the rules? I picked up (with rubber gloves) a package today from a neighbor's mailbox. It was a portion of lasagna with bechamel sauce wrapped in aluminum foil and placed in a clear plastic vegetable bag. There was a note that instructed me to heat the lasagna in the oven at 375 degrees for 30 minutes to kill any virus. True? And what about handling the plastic bag and the aluminum foil with gloves on? Necessary? Let's create some safe sharing guidelines. If we shut-in solos can't eat with friends and relatives, how can we safely cook for each other and share?

The foil-wrapped container of lasagna came from my neighbor, the noted writer, Peter Manso, who went on a home-cooking binge during the opening days of Covid. It's very sad that Peter, seemingly in fine fettle, passed away in April of 2021 from a heart attack, just as Covid appeared to be fading. RIP.

In honor of the potato as a pandemic survival food (high nutrition, long shelf life), I have been making Spanish style *tortillas*, or potato omelets. For one or two eaters, they last for days and are very good served with salads for lunch or dinner. The recipe I'm using here is based on one from a Spanish gypsy who lived in Berkeley in the 1980s, Anzonini del Puerto. He was famous in Spain, and locally, as a flamenco performer and you can see him singing and dancing in Les Blank's film, *Garlic Is As Good As Ten Mothers*. Anzonini was also a butcher and celebrated for his sausages, which he made and sold in Berkeley at the legendary Pig-by-the-tail Charcuterie in the neighborhood formerly known as the gourmet ghetto. He lived nearby for several years with Cheese Boarder Pat Darrow and they held regular fiestas that featured his dancing and singing, and his delicious versions of Spanish classics, many of which were documented by Pat. This recipe calls for lots of parsley, which I didn't have, so I added finely chopped green bell pepper for the parsley color and vegetal accent.

Anzonini's Tortilla de Patatas

Serves 2 as a main course and 4–6 as a tapa.

1 large potato, sliced thin and salted
1 onion, sliced thin
4–5 garlic cloves, sliced or chopped
1 green bell pepper, sliced thin
4–5 eggs, beaten and salted
1 cup olive oil
Salt and pepper to taste

Heat oil and fry potato slices until golden brown but not crisp. Remove the potatoes from the oil. Fry onion and bell pepper until soft and almost brown and add garlic. Continue cooking until the garlic is golden brown. (Anzonini liked the taste of well-fried, but not burnt, garlic which is rather pungent and usually frowned upon by "gourmets." I like it too.) Pour off all but ½ cup of the oil. Add potatoes and allow the fat to heat back up. Pour in the eggs and fry over medium heat, lifting edges so that the wet egg on top hits the pan and is firmed up. When set and brown on the bottom, turn over onto a flat plate. Slide the tortilla from the plate back into the pan and fry just long enough to set the egg. Transfer from the pan onto a serving plate, cut into wedges and serve hot or at room temperature.

Depending on the size of your frying pan, the tortilla can be thick or thin. You find wedges of this dish at every tapas bar in Spain. César in Berkeley makes a good one, when not shut down.

MARCH 30

RIP Saul's Deli? Saul's is closed now except for take out, but I hope not for long. It's the chicken soup for my hungry (and anxious) Jewish soul, not to mention my morning café. To think that a deli could walk such a tricky culinary/cultural line – operate as a traditional Jewish deli in the birthplace of our rather food-fussy California cuisine revolution – was, perhaps, wishful thinking, if not a fool's errand. But the owners, Peter Levitt and Karen Adelman, have pulled it off with brains and chutzpah – clever menu decisions, excellent ingredients, cooking savvy, strong management and cheerful service. Just before Covid struck, the perfect buyer for the deli emerged, vowing to carry on the tradition after decades of Karen and Peter's hard work. But the deal fell through at the last minute for obvious (Covid) reasons, forcing them to carry on. Saul's will survive, of course, and although I am truly sorry for their lost opportunity, Saul's many fans do not regret having Peter and Karen around to shepherd the deli through hard times.

Happier days at Saul's just before the Covid shut down. At left, playing with my food: A scrambled egg lady with lox, tomato, cucumber, black olive and cream cheese – à la Renaissance artist, Giuseppe Arcimboldo. At right, Saul's co-owner, Peter Levitt, cheerfully serves me one of his masterful cappuccinos.

Memory Food – Nana's lox, bagels and cream cheese: True, food can trigger lost memories, which can be very pleasant and vivid when recovered, even revelatory as we know from brain science and literature (Marcel Proust). The olfactory bulb (smell) and memory centers are closely connected on the right side of the brain. With Passover and its recitation of plagues just days away, food and memory are starting to play with each other against the backdrop of our own plague.

Proust's forgotten childhood emerged with the taste of a small teacake, a Madeleine. But, in a reversal of Proust's process, our remembered past can elevate the pleasure of food. Remembering and celebrating our long-departed family members and the foods we shared with them can transform a meal or dish into something deeply satisfying.

My memories of Nana, my paternal grandmother, are vivid. She taught me the proper way to place a single slice of lox on top of a bagel smeared with cream cheese. The trick was to spread the lox out so thinly with the back of a fork that you could see the hole of the bagel and the white of the cheese through it. Lox was a true luxury food in the 1950s and not to be eaten lightly; Nana's emphasis on frugality was, I now understand, the psychological residue of her experience of multiple life crises – immigration from Poland to San Francisco in the early 20th century; the 1906 earthquake, World War I, the Spanish flu, the Great Depression, and World War II.

Shaped by my grandmother's lesson, I prefer now the flavor of this pared-down, open face version of the Jewish classic. The ratio of fish (less) to cream cheese (more) tastes just right to me.

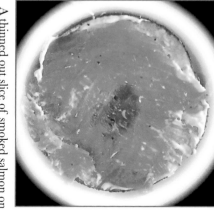

A thinned out slice of smoked salmon on half a bagel spread with cream cheese.

MAY 6

Berkeley restaurants post pandemic: When I came across this picture of Meinheit's Restaurant in Berkeley on Center Street, circa 1890, printed in the Berkeley Historical Society's brochure for their online exhibit *Berkeley's Fascination with Food*, I thought, "There it is, what restaurants will look like when they reopen – wider aisles, fewer tables spaced farther apart, fewer diners and fewer servers." Of course there were fewer people in Berkeley in 1890, fewer restaurants and going out to eat was not as common as today.

Congrats to BHS for continuing with this new exhibit during challenging times. Berkeley has always been underestimated in terms of its important contributions in many cultural realms, cuisine being one of them. The exhibit illustrates Berkeley's role in the emergence of California cuisine and the American food revolution of the 1970s-1990s. I have been asked to contribute material related to my area of expertise, garlic. The exhibit can be visited online in perpetuity on the BHS website.

Downtown Berkeley's Meinheit's Restaurant circa 1890, courtesy Berkeley Historical Society.

MAY 16

A new, improved café culture in Berkeley? I was delighted to read today about the city moving to modify selected streets and adjacent parking areas to allow restaurants and cafés to set up outdoor tables. Not only does this help save our food scene, it adds a taste of European café culture so missing here. It's obvious that the vitality of Paris cafés is due to their proximity to the life of the street. So I vote yes on this bold idea to blend our great food and coffee with the sizzle of the street. "Less cars, more tables!" And we are not alone. All across the U.S., restaurants are moving outdoors. Even London, known historically more for its private clubs than public cafés, is bringing food and beverage service out onto its sidewalks and streets, according to the *Financial Times*.

MAY 21

What about Chez Panisse? When I imagine the aftermath of Covid and the effect on our local restaurant scene, I of course worry about our California cuisine flagship. But, if any restaurant can figure out how to survive the pandemic, it's Alice Waters & Co. at Chez Panisse. They have emerged Phoenix-like from past disasters (several fires) and the restaurant has always moved forward in unexpected new directions. I expect, and pray for, no less this time around.

A drawing from 2011 on the 40th anniversary of Chez Panisse: I imagined the restaurant as a California Historical Site with a combination café, boutique, school and museum, all operated by its foundation. On the eve now of the 50th Anniversary (August 21, 2021), and in the midst of a pandemic, this fantasy of the future of the restaurant seems more possible than ever.

For Immediate Release: Taste buds set free! This is the day, "Juneteenth", that our restaurants have been allowed to reopen in the East Bay. At least, outside. Though not as culturally transformative as the day America ended slavery – to state the obvious – one can't deny that the return of public chewing – June*teeth*? – is an important marker in our Covid recovery. I jest not: it's a vitally, existentially critical day for all those splendid souls who make their livelihoods providing the delicious meals and gathering spaces we hunger for. We have been denied long enough! I happened to be picking up some food to-go at Oliveto Café and Restaurant in Rockridge and witnessed their new sidewalk seating area opening up. It was exciting and a bit surreal to see servers in masks serving diners in masks seated at outdoor tables "masked" with white tablecloths.

Oliveto's co-owner, Bob Klein, was doing his usual proprietor's amble among the tables – outdoors now – most of them still empty at 5:30 pm. He doesn't appear to have skipped a beat. His business and life partner, Maggie, was somewhere on the premises making sure, no doubt, that the flowers were just right, the menus accurate and whatever else a nearly 40 year veteran restaurateur does when dinner service begins. The fact that I went to high school with Mr. Klein and to college with Ms. Klein made this an extra special occasion for me – watching old friends doing what they do best, serving a hungry public with delicious food and good cheer alongside a dedicated and loyal staff. They are a noble and brave bunch come what may!

Co-owner Bob Klein making his table rounds again at Oliveto.

JUNE 21

Cafés and the Bolton Affaire: Cafés are coming back to life in Paris and here in the US, and not a moment too soon. We need them for our gustatory, intellectual, artistic and political health. Nice to see the important social function of cafés endorsed in the DC court's Memorandum Order of June 20, 2020, in the case of the US v. Bolton. In the ruling in favor of John Bolton's controversial anti-Trump book release (*In The Room Where It Happened*) Judge Royce C. Lamberth has, among other findings, underscored the role of cafés as an important cultural support for the practice of free speech: "A single dedicated individual with a book in hand could publish its contents far and wide from his local coffee shop."

For the judge, despite Trump's National Security Adviser's multitude of sins, it's too late to stop the presses or the mechanisms of the Bolton book's distribution: "The horse is not just out of the barn – it is out of the country," said Lamberth. A rare bit of wit and wisdom from a judicial document.

Voltaire would have been impressed by Lamberth's wit. In the Enlightenment Paris of the 1700s, cafés became the chic nexus of good taste and uncensored political speech for writers like Voltaire, Diderot and Rousseau. Revolutions have been sparked in cafés (most notably the French Revolution) and today, because of the internet, cafés serve many functions unimaginable in the 18th century including, according to Judge Lamberth, e-publishing and distribution. Though the judge can be faulted for using the somewhat antiquated American "coffee shop," he is to be applauded for his understanding of the café's crucial cultural importance.

JUNE 22

New rules: Living alone, there is no one yet in my pod or bubble to eat with. So when I go out to a newly re-opened restaurant with a friend, we'll have to sit socially distanced – six feet apart. How do you do that at a "two top" table that is at most three feet across? One way would be to pull chairs away from the table and use extra long cutlery. Williams Sonoma, are you listening?

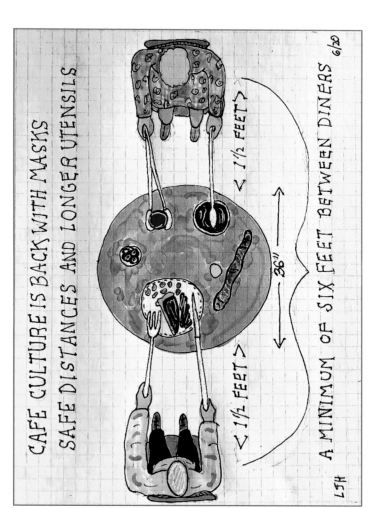

CAFÉ CULTURE IS BACK WITH MASKS
SAFE DISTANCES AND LONGER UTENSILS

< 1½ FEET >
< 1½ FEET >
36"
A MINIMUM OF SIX FEET BETWEEN DINERS
6/20
LJH

Café Culture Is Back. June 2020.

JUNE 28

Dinner is back on the table: Hard to believe, but I finally had dinner out, for the first time in three months. At Oliveto, social distancing is in place, the servers are masked, and the Covid protocols in the kitchen are being carefully honored. Risky? With the current uptick in Covid cases in Alameda Co., my cautious children responded, "Yes, too risky." Other voices were supportive – if precautions are taken. Restaurateur Bob Klein described the many safety steps they are taking and I felt reassured. He also spoke about the new chef, Peter Jackson, an alum of Jeremiah Tower's legendary Stars in SF. I know Peter and spent some time with him in Paris last summer. He has exciting plans for the new Oliveto menu, and my dinner tonight was a promising introduction: Perfect pan seared rock cod, crispy new potatoes, roasted morel mushrooms, and plump al dente asparagus, all sitting in a puddle of creamy morel-infused sauce.

Buon appetito! First dinner out
in three months at Oliveto.

JULY 14, BASTILLE DAY

Garlic Revolution on hold: On July 29, 2019, the world—not just the garlic world—was shocked when a gunman opened fire at the annual Gilroy Garlic Festival, killing several people. I posted my outrage on Facebook and the question became how Gilroy could restore confidence in a 2020 festival in the midst of an American epidemic of gun violence. No one dreamed of the coming epidemic of disease. In an exchange I had with Alice Waters soon after the massacre, I suggested that the 2020 Chez Panisse Bastille Day Garlic Festival honor not only Gilroy's victims, but also the 40th anniversary of Les Blank's film, *Garlic Is As Good As Ten Mothers* (1979) and the anniversaries of my *Book of Garlic* (1974) and Chez Panisse's first garlic festival (1976). I also proposed taking a bus full of veteran garlic activists from Berkeley down to Gilroy to show solidarity. We agreed to touch base again in the spring of 2020 to make plans, but Covid intervened.

JULY 28

Any hope for a Gilroy Garlic Festival after the violence in 2019 was dashed this year by the pandemic. But it takes more than a virus to blunt garlic's popularity. In fact, garlic joined Trump's hydroxychloroquine on lists of possible treatments for Covid. Whether or not high doses of garlic have an impact on diseases like cancer, arteriosclerosis, athlete's foot and Covid-19, its exploding popularity in the US over the last half century gave the mouthwash industry and its celebrated tag line – "Garlic breath is the worst bad breath in America"(Signal Mouthwash) – a run for its money. Our slogan, "Fight mouthwash, Eat garlic," led the charge.

A happier, more innocent time. Here I am in the late 70's with our Lovers of the Stinking Rose motto on a bumper sticker.

AUGUST 7

Paris, where are you? Hard to believe that exactly one year ago today I was making friends with a barman in Paris and learning his secrets for a great martini. Seems like just yesterday, or one hundred years ago – Covid time is so confusing! Oh, for a martini in Paris, even if their version has little to do with our English/American creation. Eric Poindron, my consulting mixologist in Paris, knows the difference, having lived in the US. He was my go-to guy at the bar of the chic Hotel Pont Royale, just up the street from my apartment. I had just been on a side trip to Venice where I had Hemingway's martini at Harry's Bar, made with the ratio of 15-1, gin to dry vermouth. I make mine the same, only with vodka instead of gin. With two cocktail onions instead of olives, it's a Gibson.

Martini variations are infinite. Is it time to rename this cocktail in line with modern variations? Here are my recommended, non-PC neologisms:*

Gitini: A classic martini made with gin and a bit of dry white vermouth.

Vokini: A classic martini made with vodka and a bit of dry white vermouth.

Vertiny: A French martini made with sweet red vermouth and a bit of gin.

Virginy: A non-alcoholic martini made with cranberry juice, a splash of tonic water and an orange twist.

Bikini: A blend of French and Anglo tastes: half vodka or gin on top, an equal amount of semi-sweet vermouth on the bottom. Serve on the rocks with a lemon or orange twist.

Dedicated to Eric Poindron

A Vertini at Café de Flore in Paris in 2019, exactly one year ago today.

SEPTEMBER 3

News from the front: Covid is back and the silence is deafening! At Cèsar in the gourmet ghetto for a pre-dinner drink and a tapas take out, I sit at a sidewalk table with a cocktail, the "Belafonte" – Uncle Nearest Tennessee whiskey, lemon, vermouth and a strawberry – served to me through an open window on the terrace. Cèsar is closed for inside seating, but there are three or four tables on the sidewalk, all empty this evening except for mine. This is Berkeley, so Cèsar is donating half the $14 price of my drink to Dine For Democracy, a get-out-the-vote organization. Bravo Cèsar!

The reduced Cèsar staff is doing their brave best to keep the vibe alive. The Cheese Board collectivists across the street are likewise making an effort, but behind their plastic cashier shields and cloth face masks I can hardly understand a word they say, let alone recognize who they are. Neighborhood chitchat is at a virtual standstill with only a smattering of anxious speculations over who will be left standing after Covid. The isolation I feel is barely tolerable. It's like a scene out of the post-apocalyptic sister film to *On The Beach*, *The Quiet Earth* (1985), where the main character notes in his log, "It seems I am the only person left on Earth."

Seated and masked at a sidewalk table outside Cèsar, I'm chatting with a server standing in the café's open window, Jim Mellgren, a journalist and co-author of Cèsar's food and cocktail books. Behind me, across the street, the pizza take-out line at the Cheese Board is back up and running.

SEPTEMBER 7—ADVERTISEMENT

Gastro-Pod – A Meals On Wheels for the Rest of Us! Most of us at-risk seniors in Berkeley are not in need enough to receive government-subsidized meals while sheltered at home. And many of us are not brave enough to dine out at our struggling pop-up street-side restaurants. But we are beyond tired enough of our home cooking and tedious curbside pickups. So what to do? Splurge with Gastro-Pod, an all-weather moveable feast sourced from your favorite restaurants. Make a reservation and our bonded, Covid-tested driver and server team will pick you up and serve your favorite restaurant meals in our classic 1947 Dodge flatbed truck, modified to host you in style. The Gastro-Pod's refrigeration unit and warming drawer will keep your food at its delicious best.

At the designated time, our crew will pick up your pod (up to six persons) and while you sip on your favorite cocktails and nibble on curated appetizers, we will chauffeur you to your preferred location – bayside, hillside, parkside. Our seats are cushy, secure and belted. Our dinnerware is ceramic and our cutlery is silverplate. Our service is attentive. The Gastro-Pod's tented top, heater units and drop-down transparent side panels are perfect for rainy and windy weather. Call now for pricing details, schedules and menus from our collaborating fine dining establishments. Let's splurge! Let's get out of the house. Let's Gastro-Pod!

OCTOBER 2

Trump tested positive for coronavirus today: I reacted by posting the Wikipedia definition of "poetic justice" on Facebook: "A literary device in which...virtue is rewarded and viciousness is punished...an ironic twist of fate related to the character's own action."

Gastro-Pod. September 2020. Cabin fever set in and I needed to find another way to feed myself. This fantasy emerged out of desperation.

NOVEMBER 7

A sea change – Biden wins! The election brought street celebrations to Berkeley (and all across the country) and hope for the future, despite the on-going Covid lockdown and our fire season's smoky darkness. The pleasures of the table may still be few and far between here in the gourmet ghetto, but we are ready to party, at least outdoors. At the French Hotel, a crowd gathered on Saturday morning after Biden wrapped up Pennsylvania. A loud boom box got everyone dancing, even me, and horns honked as cars passed by the delirious crowd. I gave my cell phone to a friend to take a picture. Note my iPhone's photo location identifier – Berkeley - Gourmet Ghetto – at the top of the photo's screen. The pre-Covid decision by the local business association to cancel the neighborhood's alleged elitist/racist moniker – gourmet ghetto – has not made its way to official online maps, nor to most of its residents who still use the ironic term affectionately.

Berkeley - Gourmet Ghetto

I'm dancing at the French Hotel after the official announcement of Biden's win on November 7.

DECEMBER 22

Announcing the Tailgate Café: I'll be parked outside Saul's Deli in North Berkeley most days in the coming weeks from about 11AM to Noon, weather and pandemic permitting. Look for me seated on the cargo deck of my station wagon, tailgate-style. I will have two folding chairs set up opposite, at least eight feet apart. Bring your own coffee and/or sandwich – Saul's offers both, curbside. Let's chat. Call in advance and I'll hold a seat.

That Saul's has had to eliminate outdoor seating because of the current surge in East Bay infections is another painful blow to our little North Berkeley community – a further insult on top of the injury of canceled indoor seating. How will deli regulars – and those like me who use the deli as our daily café – survive, let alone Saul's brave owners and remaining staff who carry on in the face of the shut down?

The idea of a tailgate café is my personal response, and a lot more practical than my Gastro-Pod fantasy. Frankly, if no one shows up "chez tailgate," that's fine. I can sit with my Saul's coffee and take-out treats while I text, draw, read, write and, most importantly, observe the comings and goings in the gourmet ghetto. This is what I do in any café, from the snazzy Café de Flore in Paris to my humble tailgate perch – observe. A flâneur on a coffee break.

My Tailgate Café outside Saul's Deli.

From the Tailgate Café I can observe the long customer line snaking its way from around the corner on Vine St. towards the Cheese Board's entrance on Shattuck Ave. Catty-corner from the Cheese Board and behind me is Saul's take-out window where Jewish comfort food is dispensed. The vibe in the hood is subdued. Sharing Saul's overcrowded sidewalk space is Masse's Pastries, always there with their fine French indulgences to go.

Up Vine to the east I can spy the Peet's Coffee line and the take-out lunch action at neighborhood newcomer, Fava. To the south on Shattuck, just past the regrettably shuttered (again) César Bar and Restaurant, is the periodic to-go action at Chez Panisse and their Sunday farmers market.

Across the street from Chez Panisse is the Sens Hotel café, still known affectionately by locals as the French Hotel. (Like "gourmet ghetto", the French Hotel moniker is part of our collective history and hard to cancel.) They are serving to-go food and coffee, but the regulars are missing in action. Among these, a fellow Francophile, the writer, Paris-trained mime and neighborhood raconteur, Leonard Pitt, who held regular "office hours" at his corner table until the shutdown.

The Cheese Board's customer line on Vine St. as it turns the corner and heads down Shattuck Ave. to the front door.

Down Vine to the West, I can see the entrance to Cafenated Coffee Company, the newest arrival in our hood. Although they are selling coffee and pastries to-go, their popular patio oasis behind the shop is closed. Imagine opening a café just as a pandemic grips the land. The real estate adage "location, location, location" has been altered by Covid to "timing, timing, timing".

I feel like I'm watching residents loading up on supplies before fleeing a foreign troop invasion. And that's what Covid is, a viral invasion. It's a sadly desolate cityscape here, but seated at the Tailgate Café I don't feel lonely. Isolated, yes, but not lonely. This, in a nutshell, is the true magic of the café – a private terroir of observation and reflection. Thomas Mann described the café experience as "the detached and elevated sphere of the literary man…" The Tailgate Café will provide some missing sociability that is the essential flip side of Mann's portrait.

The North Shattuck Association adopted the "Gourmet Ghetto" brand and started deploying marketing banners in the 1990s. In 2019, just before Covid-19's appearance, the moniker was challenged by a newly arrived shopkeeper as being racist and elitist, and the neighborhood's business association quickly – some might say too quickly – canceled the brand and removed the banners. One of the banners is on display now at the Berkeley Historical Society, a relic of a bygone era, though the name lingers on. In early 2020, Covid delivered a second blow to the neighborhood, now nameless, brandless, bannerless and almost deserted.

DECEMBER 23

A Tailgate Café scrapbook: Build it and they will come is the Hollywood film cliché, but it's also true. After announcing the Tailgate Café I tested the concept the next day. They came. Old friends, Kathy and Paul Terrell, were a chance encounter, but Marilyn Rinzler, the gourmet ghetto's former "chicken lady" at Poulet down the street, came by reservation, along with her dog Rosie. The Terrells had Masse's meringues to share. Marilyn went off to the Cheese Board to get a chocolate chip cookie. And I had a Saul's cappuccino followed by a pastrami sandwich. Fun was had by all. It's good for neighborhood business and it's good for mental health. Holiday cheers!

Left: Marilyn Rinzler and Rosie.
Right: I'm chatting with Paul
Terrell on opening day.

From Christmas 2020 through New Years 2021, visitors to the Tailgate Café made the best of their shelter-in-place lifestyle. Few of us embody the virtue of contented aloneness described by the 17th century French philosopher, Blaise Pascal. He argues in his celebrated *Pensées*, "...the sole cause of man's unhappiness is that he does not know how to stay quietly in his room." This observation is ironic given the almost simultaneous birth of café culture in Paris as the ultimate antidote to urban isolation. Paris' first café, Café Procope, was launched in 1686 by an Italian, Francesco Procopio dei Coltelli in Saint-Germain-des-Près. The French seem confused – they love French culture (especially cafés), but not so much the French people. Hence Jean-Paul Sartre's famous line from his play *No Exit*, "Hell is other people."

Of course Pascal (1623-1662) was only a child during the plague that claimed 1,000,000 French souls between 1628-1631. He never experienced the kind of cabin fever adults struggle with during a pandemic; nor was he exposed to the virtues of a café culture that arrived in Paris a few decades after his death.

Clockwise from top left: Kate Coleman, journalist and longtime hostess at Chez Panisse (retired); John Weil, publisher of the online Bay Area guide, Daily Geezer; Leonard Pitt, Paris scholar, mime and Berkeley Chocolate Club co-founder; Steve Wasserman, *bon vivant* publisher at Heyday Books.

JANUARY 1, 2021

A visit from anonymous: Guess who came to coffee to celebrate the New Year? This dear friend pulled up his hood when I was about to snap a photo to document his presence. Masks render us plenty anonymous, but one can't be too careful in the pursuit of invisibility. Most of us are less averse to exposure. In my case, I'm happy to be exposed as long as it's not my profile. I hate my profile.

JANUARY 27

Tailgate Café closes after one month: With Governor Newsom's easing of outdoor dining restrictions and Saul's tables back out on the sidewalk, I'm closing up shop. Vaccines are becoming more widely available — I got my first jab on January 21 — and we all hope this new opening will be permanent, though I will actually miss the Tailgate Café. My last customer was the children's book author Mina Witteman. We caught up on our various projects and the latest gourmet ghetto gossip.

Top: An anonymous visitor. Below: The final visitor, Mina Witteman.

If authors were chefs: My dreams are more vivid during the Covid shut down, perhaps as compensation for the loss of real life. It's as if the sleeping brain needs to fill up its tank at night with dream images to make up for the reality fuel lost during the day. The isolation has also resulted in more time for cooking and reading. I woke up this morning laughing at a dream that merged the two – literature and cookbooks. Here is the list* that evolved from the dream after breakfast:

SAMUEL BECKETT: *Waiting for Gigot*

JOSEPH CONRAD: *Lard Jim*

MICHAEL CRIGHTON: *Jurassic Pork*

CHARLES DICKENS: *The Pickle Papers*

FYODOR DOSTOEVSKY: *Cream and Punishment*

WILLIAM FAULKNER: *The Sound and the Curry*

WILLIAM GOLDING: *Lord of the Fries*

ERNEST HEMINGWAY: *For Whom the Bell Pepper Tolls*

JAMES JOYCE: *Finnegan's Cake*

HARPER LEE: *To Cook a Mockingbird*

JACK LONDON: *The Kale of the Wild*

THOMAS MANN: *The Magic Muffin*

HERMAN MELVILLE: *Moby Duck*

HENRY MILLER: *Tropic of Caramel Corn*

MARGARET MITCHELL: *Gone With The Wine*

SYLVIA PLATH: *The Bell Pepper Jar*

MARCEL PROUST: *In Search of Lost Thyme*

JEAN-PAUL SARTRE: *Beans and Nuttiness*

WILLIAM SHAKESPEARE: *Henry Ate*

JOHN STEINBECK: *Of Spice and Men*

J.R.R. TOLKEIN: *Lord of the Onion Rings*

LEO TOLSTOY: *War and Pizza*

MARK TWAIN: *Huckleberry Flan*

JOHN UPDIKE: *Rabbit Reduction*

VOLTAIRE: *Candied*

KURT VONNEGUT: *Breakfast of Champignons*

ALICE WALKER: *The Collard Purple*

OSCAR WILDE: *The Pitcher of Dorian's Gravy*

Following the posting of the list on social media, friends responded with some great titles of their own. If you remove the celebrity authors from some of my titles, they sound like pretty good cookbooks. *The Kale of the Wild*, *Of Spice and Men* and *The Pickle Papers* all could be commercial winners.

*This list was subsequently published by the online magazine, *Reinventing Home*.

MARCH 5

At Julia's Restaurant in the Berkeley City Club Hotel, located near the campus on Southside, I had a much-anticipated restaurant meal with a friend, seated together on the hotel's reopened and socially distanced outdoor terrace. Hard to believe that a year of seeing restaurant openings and closings are – one can always hope – finally at an end. Julia's, hidden away in this Julia Morgan-designed "Little Castle," is one of the few remaining bastions of sophisticated French-leaning cuisine in Berkeley. My inner food blogger, stymied by Covid-related restaurant chaos, has been dying to express some opinions, so here I go: First, the meal was delicious, elegantly served and reasonably priced. A very pleasant, perfectly paced, old school dining experience. But even more noteworthy, Julia's roast chicken, available for curbside pick up only, is totally sublime and gives Chez Panisse's excellent herb-stuffed take-out bird a run for its money as the best in the East Bay. Take-out chicken has been a Covid staple Chez Moi, and Julia's whole bird, with haricots verts and roasted potatoes included, is enough for 2-4 persons. A great value during hard times. In my solo condition, several days of Julia's leftover chicken permutations – chicken salad, soup makings, etc. – are a real bonus. But don't tell anyone!

The seared scallops at Julia's were served on a bed of diced vegetables, sitting in a pool of *jus* (left). Sharon Rudnick (right), vaccinated and with mask down, starts with a pureed vegetable soup, topped with a *crème fraîche* garnish, and a crouton on the side.

The gourmet ghetto loses a beloved founder*

Elizabeth Valoma (Aka Meg Avedisian),

Co-founder of the Cheese Board Collective

March 10, 1930-April 24, 2021

As Covid took its toll in early 2020 and our social lives contracted further in the fall, I tried to stay in touch with 90-year-old Elizabeth without in any way burdening her as her condition became increasingly fragile. Bringing her food had been one avenue of contact, and a Saul's bagel delivery I offered her around her March birthday seemed to work as a token replacement for the Saul's bagels and lox eating ritual we had enjoyed for years.

Bagels were symbols, really, of our shared bond with Jewishness – the secular/culinary variety. Israel and Elizabeth's time on a kibbutz with her husband, Sahag Avedisian, in the 60s were the inspiration for the Cheese Board's incorporation as a worker-owned collective. Despite being proud of her Armenian heritage, Elizabeth was a true daughter of Israel. In an email thanking me for my bagel offer she added the following prophecy:

I'm managing… 90 years isn't easy… I'm enjoying life… But unable to hug and kiss…I hate that… This virus won't be gone before I vanish…

She was right. She signed off the email: "Joy and Love". Which is what she brought to all of us – family, friends and community.

*A longer version of this remembrance was posted on Facebook and then published in *Berkeley Times* on May 6, 2021.

Elizabeth Valoma at my house in 2017.

First day back at Saul's: They took longer than most restaurants to reopen despite high vaccination rates in Alameda County. Berkeley had announced approval for 50% indoor occupancy back in March. Note in the photo my tin coffee cup with a Peet's logo. Saul's owners are still not ready to reintroduce their ceramic cups, so I pour Saul's disposable cup of Joe (made with Mr. Espresso beans from Oakland) into my Peet's cup. The staffing is not at a level that can handle the new demand, so all ordering and payment is via the cell phone app, *Toast*. Humans bring the food and bus the tables, and it's good to be with humans again. It's not yet the Saul's food and service of old. But for the moment, I'm delighted to be back at my corner table with my coffee, my newspaper and my journal.

Which is the perfect time to bring my Plague Diner's Diary to a close. My plague year began and ended on the days Saul's closed in 2020 and opened again in 2021 – *my* plague year, it must be emphasized, not the plague itself. That plague is on going, alas, and only time – Covid time – will tell us when it's over.

At the re-opened Saul's Deli, I'm back, hopefully for good, at my corner table #23.

EPILOGUE

For practically from the start of spring in the year we mentioned above [1348],
the plague began producing its sad effects in a terrifying and extraordinary manner.

— Giovanni Boccaccio, *The Decameron*

In the spring of 2021, one year after I started tracking pandemic time with a sprouting potato, I had the eerie feeling I was living with an obnoxious, possibly homicidal houseguest – Mr. Covid-19. My domestic lord/butler bubble had been invaded by a toxic tenant I could not evict. Enough was enough. Tailgate cafés, Trump MAGA hat projects, diary keeping, image making – all these "creative" tasks were feeling absurdly Sisyphean, and wearing thin.

To offset this melancholy state of affairs, I reached out to a group of friends to start a Zoom book group. I proposed that we take turns presenting chapters from *The Decameron*, Giovanni Boccaccio's mostly comic, sometimes tragic collection of stories set in the time of the Black Death. It seemed a relevant parallel – Florence and Berkeley – for understanding, and surviving, our isolated pandemic lives. We were not alone. I came across other *Decameron* groups on the internet that had emerged during the on and off again Covid lockdowns, which supported my impulse to gather around Boccaccio. Whoever gets the profits from this renaissance of *Decameron* popularity – no doubt the most recent translator, Wayne Rebhorn, and his publisher, Norton – must be very happy. Boccaccio and his heirs, may they rest in peace, would be pleased.

In Boccaccio's novel, the ten characters (seven young women, three young men) all privileged Florentines, escape the ravages of the Black Death in 1348 by retreating to a villa just outside Florence to tell stories over the course of two weeks. They eat delicious food, dance, sing, read poems and cavort in nature – a Zoom *au naturel.*

Each character is given a day to tell stories taken by Boccaccio from Italian, French and Latin sources, and from local oral tradition. The allegorical tales cover the gamut of human behavior, and misbehavior. Many are hilarious and ribald; others subtle and enigmatic. The Catholic Church's hypocrisy and Florence's upper class avarice get the brunt of Boccaccio's satirical pen, making his *Decameron* controversial in its day and "modern," the medieval equivalent of sex, drugs and rock and roll. Boccaccio's intention is to have his characters replicate and preserve the social structures and values of Florence from a safe, paradisiacal vantage point outside the city, while within Florence the bubonic plague tears everything apart.

When we launched our *Decameron* group, we were channeling Boccaccio's mission from the safety of our Zoom's virtual country villa – replicating and preserving Berkeley's social structures and shared values we were cut off from by Covid. Everything, that is, but the feasting and dancing and cavorting in nature. Eventually, we thought, with the vaccine's arrival, Berkeley would open up again and we could return to our actual lives (with feasting, dancing and cavorting).

On the last day of our book group, we broke out of our virtual universe and met in the garden of one of our Zoom mates to celebrate with appetizers, wine and a closing discussion of our experience together. Social distance was honored – despite our being fully vaccinated – but it was, finally, actual not virtual. We were the flower children of the Berkeley 60s and 70s now inhabiting, 50 years later, a darker universe. We wondered what our lives would be like when the pandemic finally passed. We all believed that nothing would ever be the same.

As new waves of the interwoven variants of Delta and Trumpism emerged in the weeks and months that followed our garden party, the group began to consider another book group Zoom, and other books – Chaucer's *Canterbury Tales* was high on the list, a book influenced by Boccaccio's "frame tale" narrative structure – stories within stories. And I began to consider launching volume two of my journal. But we'll see what happens. As Boccaccio put it in an amusing comment near the end of *The Decameron*: "I acknowledge...that the things of this world are completely unstable and endlessly changing – which could explain what happened with my tongue." For now, I will hold mine.

Berkeley, California
September 26, 2021

September 2021. Since the last photo in June, my potato clock appears to have maintained its shape, but all hints of green in the sprouts are gone. It seems frozen in Covid time. Petrified.

ACKNOWLEDGEMENTS

I would like to sincerely thank all those generous souls who helped me turn my Covid journal into a book. Kaaren Kitchell, Susan Griffin, Darryl Henriques, Marion Abbott, Tom Farber, Celik Kayalar, Ashley Crnkovich and Valerie Andrews offered helpful comments on the material, as did Ann Arnold who copy edited the manuscript. Agent Peter Beren was generous with advice on various aspects of publication. I am grateful to Ashley Ingram for her elegant book design and to Lily LeaVesseur who assisted me with the book's production. Thanks to Brad Bunnin, Nenelle Bunnin, Jane Ellis, Jeremiah Tower and John Weil who critiqued a PowerPoint version of the book and gave me encouragement.

To *The Decameron* book group I owe a debt of gratitude for the companionship and smart repartee while reading Boccaccio together: Sharon Rudnick, Pamela Prince, Gloria Polanski, Jean-Luc Szpakowski, Hilary Roberts, Suzanne Pregerson and Frank Werblin.

To all the brave restaurateurs, chefs, servers and purveyors who kept me eating well indoors and out – and to-go – during my plague year, I am eternally grateful: Bob and Maggie Klein and staff at Oliveto; Peter Levitt and Karen Adelman and staff at Saul's Deli; Alice Waters and staff at Chez Panisse; The Cheese Board Collective; Julia's restaurant at the Berkeley City Club; the gourmet ghetto's many fine eating and drinking establishments: César, Corso, Masse's Pastry, Peet's, Poulet and Tigerlily; and the North Berkeley and Kensington farmers markets.

To my Tailgate Café visitors, thanks for bringing light into the middle of the tunnel.

Warm appreciation to Marilyn Rinzler for our neighborhood walks; to Steve Khan for our Sunday telephone catch-ups; and to Michele Perrella for our putting competitions at Tilden Park Golf Course.

To my Facebook friends, I truly appreciated your comments and likes as my pandemic musings and images were posted.

All my love to my family – Max, Alex, Linda, Alison, Allie, Ana and Matt – who nourished me on many levels during our shared plague year. The bocce ball brunches were a lifesaver.

ABOUT THE AUTHOR

Photo by Dillon Vado

L. John Harris is a writer, artist, publisher and filmmaker. He is Curator of the Harris Guitar Collection at the San Francisco Conservatory of Music. His previous books include *The Book of Garlic*; *Foodoodles: From the Museum of Culinary History*; and *Café French: A Flâneur's Guide to the Language, Lore and Food of the Paris Café*. His films include *Divine Food: One Hundred Years in the Kosher Delicatessen Trade* and *Los Romeros: The Royal Family of the Guitar*.

Mr. Harris divides his time between Berkeley and Paris. His next book will focus on the history of Berkeley's "gourmet ghetto" as the epicenter of the California/American food movement of the 1970s and 80s.

Villa Books
1569 Solano Ave. #201
Berkeley, CA
94707
www.ljohnharris.com
ljohnharris2021@gmail.com

127